How to be Rich

How to be Rich

The Small Business Owner's Guide to Attracting Customers and Clients

CHUCK J. RYLANT

PERFECT LIFE PUBLISHING

www.ChuckRylant.com

ISBN 10: 0-9839637-3-8
ISBN 13: 978-0-9839637-3-8

Published by:
Perfect Life Publishing
793 Foothill Boulevard, Suite 165
San Luis Obispo, CA 93405-1683

Book Design by:
Jerry & Michelle Dorris
Authorsupport.com

Introduction

Most small-business marketing sucks, and if you are willing to be honest, you probably do not have a reliable marketing system that dependably delivers new and returning customers or clients.

Most business owners are floundering when it comes to advertising and marketing because they have never been exposed to the fundamentals of direct response marketing.

Many small-business owners and solopreneurs struggle as they repeatedly make the same mistakes. They are working harder at the wrong things, which traps them in the same discouraging situations.

If you can relate, it is not your fault.

Most of the "advice" you get from people selling advertising is wrong, and everything you see the big companies doing is not right for you.

Rarely does the small-business owner, the local merchant, or even the owner of a midsize company launch their venture focused on the single most important subject that leads to business success—marketing.

Typically the owner opens up shop as an expert in their field or a practitioner of their craft, but rarely do they understand what goes into a predictable and repeatable marketing system.

But there is no reason to reinvent the wheel or continue struggling, because prosperous entrepreneurs have used this formula successfully for decades.

After reading this entertaining story, you will never look at an ad, promotion, website, or flyer in the same way. Through an entertaining novel, you will come to understand the common mistakes that cost business owners countless sleepless nights and piles of money wasted on bad advertising.

Regardless of whether you are selling a product or a service, this style of marketing will enable you to skip years of trial and error. You will discover how to refocus on what will actually attract ideal customers, clients, or patients who are ready to do business with you without price resistance.

One

The large rollup door was raised at Parson's Auto Repair, which was tucked away in the corner of a strip of industrial garages in the small town on the California coast. It was darker than usual inside the garage when old man Walter shuffled past the sign sternly prohibiting customers from entering the mechanics' bay.

Walter strolled right past David, the shop owner, whose head was buried under the hood of a maroon BMW. The import was one of only two cars in the shop. The other was a 1967 Camaro sitting on cement blocks in the garage corner. It was hard to see the classic car's color under the thick layer of dust.

Walter did not notice David as he walked by, but he would not have stopped anyway—not before getting his morning coffee. The lobby area was clean, with carpet and upscale furniture, but the shop area had a worn oil-stained concrete floor. As Walter walked into the desolate front office and stared bleakly into the empty coffee pot, he grumbled, "Where is everyone?"

How to be Rich — Chuck Rylant

"Dammit!" David's voice came from the garage.

Walter grunted and shuffled back out there.

David was gripping his hand and shaking it from just having slammed it into the car's aluminum engine block, clamping his jaw to keep from continuing to curse. The wrench he'd been using had slipped out of his hand, and he and Walter listened to it, clank clank clank, as it fell through the engine compartment, bouncing off the inner fender before splashing right into the oil basin below. *Dammit!* David's internal dialog got increasingly colorful.

Walter surveyed him without much sympathy. "What's with the lights?" he asked. "Might be easier to work in here if you could see what you were doing."

David wrapped an old, oily shop towel around his hand to contain the oozing blood from the gash. "There's enough light with the shop doors open."

"Didn't you pay your electric bill?" Walter prodded.

David rolled his eyes to avoid answering. "Get your coffee, old man."

"I would if anyone had made any. Is this how you treat your loyal customers?"

Startled, David looked to the office, where the lights were dim, and then to the clock. Where was Molly, his office manager? *Oh, yeah, that "day off."* What he asked aloud was, "When have you ever been a customer?"

David headed for the front desk to dig through the parts catalog for a new Beemer water pump. He'd have to break the news to Mr. Freedman that his repair estimate had to be revised—upward. A smear of blood splashed across the page, as blood soaked through the saturated rag. David refused to learn to use the online catalog even though the printed ones were becoming hard to find. Normally, Molly ordered parts, but today David was stuck doing it.

"I've been meaning to bring Elaine's car in," Walter said, right behind him.

"You've been saying that since we met at the country club. How many years ago was that?"

"I'm getting old and I forget," Walter grinned. "Cut me some slack."

"You don't forget how to find your way to free coffee," David said. He threw the catalog onto the counter in frustration and tugged the rag tighter to his hand. "If you keep hanging around, I'm putting you to work."

"You should do something about that hand," Walter said. "It's leaving a trail."

"It's fine. I have bigger things to worry about." David had not meant to let that slip. He was more worried than he let on.

But Walter joked back, "I'm going to have to find you some customers."

David wondered if it was that obvious. The last thing he wanted was anyone else to know just how bad business was. "Isn't it about time for your afternoon nap?"

"Don't put me out to pasture just yet," Walter said. "I've still got a little left in me."

Two

David had forgotten how hungry he was until he got home late that night, when he opened the door and was hit with the residual smell of Jennifer's spaghetti. He walked into the kitchen of their three-bedroom home, hoping to find some leftovers. Instead, when he hit the light switch, he found a pile of mail stacked on the kitchen table. Bills.

Just what I need, David thought.

As Jennifer came down the stairs, David squirted gritty green hand glop on his hands at the kitchen sink. His injury from that morning, which had given him no more trouble once it stopped bleeding, began to throb as he scrubbed the grease away. It would heal, though, just like the many others he had acquired turning wrenches over the years.

"I ate without you," Jennifer said. "I fixed you a plate and put it in the microwave."

Ah. He had not remembered to check there. "Thanks," David said. "I will enjoy your lovely dinner in the company of these bills."

He wished he could ignore the stack of "payment dues" staring up at him, but ignoring them had gotten him into this mess. Most of the shop bills went to their house because Jennifer, his bookkeeper-slash-wife, preferred to settle their accounts at home. David had not seen a steady paycheck since he left his job at the dealership four years ago. He hated the money rollercoaster, but stringing creditors along had become a normal part of business.

"Long day?" Jennifer asked.

David nodded while rummaging through the mail. There was a never-ending supply of bad news hiding in those envelopes. Bills were just more stress on top of the existing weight he carried on his shoulders.

"It's ten o'clock," Jennifer said with a bit of an interrogative tone. She didn't like David's long hours, but she did her best to be supportive.

"No mechanics today," he said. "And remember? I had Molly take the day off to reduce payroll this week. Without her covering the office, I could not get a damn thing done until after closing." The employees needed the money as much as he did, but he was cutting corners everywhere he could.

"Did any work come in?" Jennifer asked.

"Only Walter. He's like a stray dog," David said, laughing at his own joke.

"Why do you put up with him?" Jennifer asked.

"Aw, he's just an ornery old man with nothing better to do but pester me. I hope someone's as nice to me when I'm his age." David paused for a moment. "He's harmless, but today he was hassling me about the lights and the staff. It was a little annoying."

Jennifer rubbed his arm. "Doesn't he realize that could be a sensitive subject? You're working so hard."

"He's old, but he's not dumb—I just don't think 'feelings' are his specialty." David shrugged. "And the shop might be struggling, but I'm not closing. I'll figure it out."

Before David opened the shop, he thought honesty and good service would be all it took to succeed. He was now learning the hard way that it took much more. What exactly, though, he was not sure. David was the most experienced mechanic in town, but he knew he was faking it as a business owner. And being passionate about protecting his customers from unscrupulous shops that rip people off was not enough. If David could not keep the doors open, he would be no help to anyone.

Walter might not know, but Jennifer knew exactly why the lights were off. She was the one who had inherited the role of David's bookkeeper. It was a no-win position. She did her best to support David, but she saw how bad off they were when she paid the shop's monthly expenses. Usually there was more going out than coming in.

Jennifer loaded the dishwasher while he ate. "Anything there about Zack's tuition?"

In fact, there was. But David did not want to talk about it. He slid that letter to the bottom of the stack. "I'll take care of it."

Jennifer's forehead creased, but she did not look at him.

"I promise," David said, hoping to make her worry go away. "I stayed late to finish the clutch on that BMW. That money will help."

"What about payroll?" Jennifer asked. Recently they had agreed that using income from her own job was not a good solution. Their savings had also dwindled to the point of alarm. It had been causing tension in their marriage.

"Payroll. Right." David had already mentally spent the money from the clutch job. His moment of calm after bolting the BMW back together was already gone. They were going in circles.

I've got to get us out of this hole, he thought.

Three

David got to work late the next morning after another sleepless night. Molly, thank goodness, was already there and had the coffee brewing.

"Hey, there!" she said, unfailingly cheery as always.

David winced good-naturedly. "Turn the volume down on that thing."

Molly laughed and waved some printouts at him. "I want to show you the new logos. I think they're looking good!"

After college, Molly had been a graphic designer for an award-winning advertising firm in Southern California. She had loved her job, but after five years she was tired of the big-city hustle. She wanted to come back to her quaint little hometown.

David knew Molly was overqualified the first day they met, but he liked the idea of having an office manager. He could not really afford her, especially given with what she had been earning in the big city, but that did not keep him from trying to keep her around. If she could spare him from office chores, he could do what he enjoyed—working on cars.

Molly agreed to a pay cut for a less-demanding schedule, and David hoped the shop might grow by tapping her advertising experience. Molly had quickly adjusted to her role as office manager, creating order in the shop that did not previously exist, but her real passion was creative work. She had been prodding David about designing branded material to promote the business, but he was usually too busy putting out fires to deal with it.

Now here she was, with another round of designs. David did not know what he wanted precisely, but he could always tell what he did not like. And it would show on his face.

Molly had been surprised by how picky David was about the logo. Before she joined the shop, he was using free business cards from an online template. But it had taken several revisions to get them to here. What would he say this time?

David looked over what she handed him and paused for a moment. Molly waited anxiously.

"I love it!" he said, surprising even himself.

"Really?" Molly asked. "Finally?"

David traced the outline of the image thoughtfully. "Yes! It's capturing something about us somehow."

"Great!" Molly said. "Now I can work on a tri-fold brochure."

Oh, yeah, that brochure. David hoped her idea of a new brochure and business cards would be a big step toward bringing in the money for Zack's tuition. Then he mentally face-palmed. *Damn! That letter.*

He grabbed his backpack and went out to the shop. Rummaging around, he pulled out the letter from where he'd stuffed it before going to bed. The grim reality of it was a shock. "Final Notice" was stamped big and bold and red on the top of the first sheet. Past due notices were nothing new, but this letter said that if Zack's registration fees were not paid in two weeks, he would not be able to register that semester.

David had already been losing sleep over the tuition bill because it was money he did not have. His own father had not gone to college, nor had he encouraged David to enroll. David always felt that missing college was why he struggled in his own business. He was determined to provide Zack with a better start than his own.

But how was he going to make that happen?

Four

That afternoon, Walter made his way back through the shop door on his way home from his "rounds."

"Hello, Walter!" Molly called brightly, as she adjusted the holder on the counter with her freshly printed, elegant tri-fold brochures and a handful of David's new matching business cards. The brochure, trimmed in blue, looked professional, especially with its stock photos of attractive people smiling next to cars.

Walter's hand was on the coffee pot as he did a double take.

"What have you got there?" he asked gruffly.

David strolled in from the garage, wiping his hands on a rag. "Oh, just the next phase in getting the word out."

Lips pursed, Walter shuffled over with his Styrofoam cup to take a look. He peered at the brochure through squinted eyes.

David and Molly held their breath. There was no telling what he would say.

"New logo looks good..." Walter said finally.

David and Molly started breathing again.

"…but the logo and brochure aren't worth squat."

David stood there surprised, while Molly began to get defensive.

"What do you mean?" she asked. "It's just like the ones I would do in LA."

"For big companies, right?" Walter asked.

"Yes," she asserted. "Big, successful companies."

"Well, this place isn't that."

"All right, all right," David said.

"'Where excellence comes first,'" Walter mimicked as he read the brochure's headline. "You're not getting rich with that one."

Molly turned to David with a hurt look. It was her writing, and they'd both liked it. David rose to her defense.

"I think it's great," David said. "What's wrong with it?"

"Of course excellence comes first," Walter said. "Customers expect that."

"It's just a slogan!" David snapped back. "No one reads that anyway."

"Exactly," Walter said. "Put something in there they'll pay attention to."

"Like what?" David asked.

"Bait."

"Bait? What are you talking about?" David had had enough. "You're losing it."

"I could give you some pointers—"

David took one look at Molly's still-hurt face and cut him off, "Not today, thanks. See you later."

Walter shrugged and headed out the door, shaking his head the whole time.

"What was that all about?" Molly asked once he was gone. She liked Walter, but it was hard not to take his banter personally.

David reassured her. "He doesn't know what he's talking about." *At least, I hope he doesn't.*

Five

David committed himself one hundred percent to the new marketing materials. During the next week, he handed out a business card and brochure to anyone who would tolerate it. He did not enjoy shoving cards in everyone's face, but how else were they going to get out there? He posted a brochure on the corkboard at the country club and gave one to all his friends, hoping they would share it with their friends.

Eventually, David had handed out a couple hundred cards and brochures in total and had no idea where to turn next. His initial enthusiasm had run out faster than it took to print the things, and by the end of the week, he was losing sleep again.

"What is it, David?" Jennifer asked sleepily, trying to hide her annoyance that David was tossing and turning at three in the morning.

"Nothing," David said. "I didn't mean to wake you."

"Well, I'm awake now," Jennifer persisted.

"It's these business cards," David said. "And Walter."

"Walter?" Jennifer asked. "What does he have to do with anything?"

"Walter gave me grief about the brochure."

"When?"

"When we first made them. It's been eating at me all week."

"That's keeping you up?" Jennifer asked. "You two bicker like a couple of teenage girls. Sometimes people are just jerks. The brochures look nice. I'm sure they will help."

It was not Walter's tone that had been bothering him. It was that David had begun to worry that Walter might have been right. Not a single new customer had come through the door at Parson's Auto since he started passing out his new promotional material. David was still stuck in the same rut.

Six

David's mood perked up when he got to the shop the next morning and heard an air ratchet snapping away. As usual, Molly had gotten there before David, and thankfully there was enough work lined up that he had brought both mechanics in for the day.

David's shop had grown from the days when he was a one-man show. The other mechanics helped him keep up when he needed them, but they also added to his payroll anxiety.

"What's on the board today?" David asked.

"Two oil changes, a 100,000-mile service, and we're starting a water pump on the Audi," Molly said. "Mrs. Clark's car is still here too."

"The Mercedes? Is she ready to have her cylinder heads fixed?" David asked with optimism. "Her car's been here in pieces for at least a week."

"I think she's worried about the cost," Molly said. "They might buy a new car because this one needs so many repairs."

David stared at the office wall for a moment, running numbers in his head. Without the cylinder-head repair, they could break even for the day and maybe cover payroll, but if he stayed late and did Mrs. Clark's job himself, he might bring in enough to make a payment on Zack's tuition.

"Oh, look, *she's* here again," Molly said, nodding at the Cadillac in the parking lot.

David snapped out of his trance. The infamous Sharon was climbing out of her pink Caddy. She had seen him arrive and now waved to him through the window. He waved back, wondering if she used to sell makeup before she got in the advertising business. She had been stalking David for a few weeks, trying to get a meeting.

Sharon was a big lady with a loud business blazer and heavy makeup to match. David watched her struggle to lock the car with her long, shiny fingernails. His mind wandered for a moment while he questioned why she needed the twenty or so random key chains she had dangling there.

"Wish you could tell her I'm not here," David said as he watched Sharon put the keys in her purse.

"You've dodged her three times," Molly said. "Maybe she can promote our new logo and get the word out about the shop."

Molly actually wanted to see David use the logo in an advertising campaign like the type she had designed when she worked in Los Angeles. David had resisted. But now, after the brochure had gone nowhere, he was curious to see if advertising was the answer. A few minutes later, Sharon was sitting across from David at his desk.

"So!" Sharon said. "What's your advertising program look like at the moment?"

She was a bit brash for David's liking, and he did not want to admit the answer was "none, really," so he deflected the question by asking what type of advertising she offered. Sharon droned on about the company she worked for, the media they used, and awards the company had received.

"What's your marketing budget?" she asked without any hesitation. "What are you prepared to spend?"

"Um," David said a bit flustered. *Nothing? How does "nothing" sound?* "I'm not sure how much I want to spend right now."

"We'll start with your marketing budget so we know what we have to work with," Sharon said.

Sharon showed David various options in the yellow pages, newspaper spots, mailers, and radio, and even mentioned the internet. When she revealed the price options, David inwardly cringed.

"I'm going to have to think about it," he said, while looking at sample ads. The options were overwhelming, and he did not want to admit how naïve he felt about the whole conversation.

The bells over the door jingled, and in walked Walter. Molly tried to head him off, but as he lingered over the coffee pot, David could tell he was eavesdropping. *The man needs a life*, David thought as he turned his attention back to Sharon.

"The more you invest, the more exposure we can bring to your brand," Sharon said.

She was talking awfully loud. David tried to bring the conversation to a more private level. "Exposure, right," he practically whispered to keep Walter from hearing.

Sharon did not take the hint. "You want something bigger than your competitors so your prospects will recognize your business. The more you invest, the more brand recognition you'll create."

Out of the corner of his eye, David saw Walter shake his head as he stirred in the powdered cream stuff.

"We could put you in this newspaper three times per week," Sharon continued as she filled in her order sheet. "It has readers throughout the coast. The longer you commit, the less expensive it will be. The deadline for the next round is Tuesday. Do you want the whole-page or half-page ad?" She went straight to "assuming the close" and started punching numbers into the calculator that magically appeared out of nowhere.

David squirmed. "I'm not sure I'm ready to start."

"Don't worry," Sharon said. "I'll make it easy for you. We'll handle the design and everything. Just leave it to me."

That's not what's bothering me, David thought, his mind on his bank account. His instinct was to wait and think about it, but he looked around the quiet shop and wanted more than anything to have it filled with cars and customers.

Sharon kept talking. She sweetened the deal, offering to waive the design fee and assign her "award-winning" graphic designer to David's ad. "That level of service isn't available to everyone," she said. "You can have it for no extra charge, but only if you finalize the contract right now."

Finalize, as in give you a check, David thought. He squirmed. Where would that money come from?

Then another voice broke in.

"He doesn't want it," Walter squawked, coffee in hand.

How to be Rich — Chuck Rylant

David's jaw dropped. *What is he talking about?*

Sharon sat up straight and turned slowly to icily look Walter straight in the eye. "And you are...?"

"A friend. But I couldn't help overhearing your sales pitch."

David waved his hand at Walter, dismissing him, but Walter ignored it.

"With all due respect, sir," Sharon said, "this might not be your area of expertise."

Walter snorted. "I'm not so sure of that, sweetheart."

Sharon's eyebrows rose practically to her hairline.

David looked over at Molly, who stood gaping in place like a deer in the headlights. He got up and ushered Walter toward the door. "Thanks for your help, Walter."

Walter talked into David's ear as David shoved him out the door. "Don't give her a check!"

David just shook his head as the door jingled shut. He turned back to Sharon. "Sorry about that. He hangs out here sometimes."

At least Sharon did not seem to be taking offense. "Oh, not to worry," she said. "Some people just don't understand the power of advertising. Now, where were we?" With a forgiving, expectant, toothy smile, she clicked her pen open and held it out to David.

Seven

J ennifer ate lunch at her desk in her office at the engineering firm. She usually ate with friends, but today was the day to get David's payroll out, and there was that morning's email from the bank she had not had the chance to look at yet.

David's bookkeeping was becoming increasingly irritating because there was never enough money to totally cover expenses. There were only a few times in the past three years where they had a comfortable margin in the bank account, and the last time was months ago. Now, bookkeeping was a game of shuffling bills by due dates.

Jennifer tapped away at the calculator while entering a list of numbers on her yellow pad. She was becoming an expert at stretching dollars as far as possible, but today that was not going to work. She decided to double check the balance online.

Once she logged into the account, though, she got a nasty surprise.

"What?" She was surprised enough to exclaim this aloud. "Overdraft coverage? They took the money from savings?"

How to be Rich — Chuck Rylant

A few clicks later, she had the culprit. A check from David to some advertising place. Where had that come from? The check processed one day after he wrote it. She could not make payroll on time, let alone deal with the other bills. It would not be so bad if they were not already struggling to make it on her income alone, but more often than not, she funneled money from her personal account to pay David's business expenses. This time, the bank had taken the amount directly from their linked account.

Lips tight, Jennifer picked up the phone and dialed the shop. "Hi, Molly, is David around?"

Molly's eyebrows rose at her abrupt tone. That was weird for Jennifer. "No, he's out on a test drive," Molly said. "Is there anything I can help with?"

"Do you know anything about this advertising expense?" Jennifer did not usually involve Molly in the finances, but she also wanted to get to the bottom of this—quickly. "I've never seen this bill."

"Oh, yes!" Molly answered enthusiastically. "Our first ad is coming out on Monday! He used the new logo and everything."

Jennifer knew Molly was very proud of that logo. "Oh, really?" Jennifer said, softening her tone. "That's interesting."

"Didn't he tell you? He was real excited about it."

"I'll bet he was." Jennifer's mind raced. Molly's answer ruined any chance that this was a bank error, a hope Jennifer had had even though she could see David's signature right on the check image online.

"Should I tell him you called?" Molly asked to break the silence.

"That would be great."

Eight

"What do you mean you thought you could cover it?"

Jen's voice went into that high register David dreaded. He had not called her back, and now they were arguing at home. He got defensive. "Hon, it just got away from me. We have some work on a Mercedes that I thought would be enough."

"David, that was a huge check. Why didn't you consult with me first?"

"I know how to run my own business, Jen." David slapped the kitchen towel onto the counter. He had just gotten home from another long day of too much work and not enough money. He had thought the check would take several days to clear, but because Sharon's company used the same bank he did, the money had transferred almost instantaneously.

Jennifer's face looked hurt. "I thought we were partners in this, David. I thought we were working together."

David blew out a breath. "I know, I know. I should have spoken to you first. The deal was just too good. And Molly is sure it will bring in new business, which we really need."

How to be Rich — Chuck Rylant

"So what do we do now? I don't think we have enough to cover payroll. There's the tuition bill coming soon, too."

David did not pick that moment to tell her it was already there. "Let me get through this week," he said. "I think what we have in the shop will be enough. Monday will start a whole new phase of growing the business."

Jen looked doubtful, but she let him take her into his arms. "I'm just worried," she said into his chest as he hugged her.

He held her tighter. "Have faith in me. It'll work out."

Jen gave a shuddering sigh and did not answer.

Nine

Promptly at nine Monday morning, Walter drove up to the shop in his wife's convertible BMW.

David watched him from inside the bay where he was running through the day's details with the two mechanics. He wiped his hands on a rag. He could not help smiling. Today was the day the ad came out. David could not wait for the results.

Walter marched over, newspaper tucked under his arm. He walked right by a car suspended from the ground with a mechanic removing its wheels.

"Good morning!" he called to David.

"Here for your coffee?"

"Nope. Today I thought I'd finally bring Elaine's car in."

David was surprised. Walter had been talking about that forever, but David never thought he would actually do it. "What's it need done?"

"How should I know?" Walter shrugged. "You're the expert."

David rolled his eyes. "I thought you knew everything."

"Everyone has their own areas of expertise. Yours is cars."

David played along. "What's yours then? Coffee machines?"

Walter gave him a mock glare. "Not quite." Walter opened up the newspaper to a page way in the back, to the bottom inside right corner where David's one-eighth page ad was surrounded by what looked like a million other ads. "I saw your ad this morning."

David frowned. It had been the largest ad he could afford, and there on the page it did not look like much. But he said, "There, see? Working already."

Walter snorted. "So where are the hordes of new customers?"

"Look, Walter—"

"In fact, I'd be surprised if anyone comes in at all."

"It just came out!"

"Doesn't matter. Won't work."

David's irritation grew. "You're some kind of expert?"

Walter's eyebrows shot up, but all he said was, "I know a thing or two."

David bit his lip to keep from making a sharp retort. He took a breath. "I'll take a look at Elaine's car and let you know what it needs."

"Yeah, okay. Whatever you say." Walter glanced around at the cars in the parking lot. "Can I have a loaner? I wanted to hit some balls."

David could see Walter's clubs sticking up from the BMW's back seat. "You know we don't do loaners."

"Okay then, give me a lift up there."

An hour later, David found himself at the golf club with Walter in the middle of the week.

Ten

David and Walter chatted on the way up to the country club. David was distracted anyway. He was not sure ferrying Walter around was the best use of his time. But Walter blathered on about who he had been golfing with lately and how great it was. David was disappointed that he had not been able to go for months and only listened with half an ear.

They pulled into the parking lot. As David heaved Walter's clubs out of the back, Walter pointed at the other neglected bag of clubs shoved into the SUV's trunk space. It practically had cobwebs on it.

"Haven't gone in a while?" Walter asked.

"Too busy." David grunted as he dropped Walter's bag onto the ground.

"How about we play a round? Don't want to lose your edge."

David's game had probably evaporated long ago. "I don't know—"

"Unless you think you can't beat an old man."

Actually, David rationalized, *that would probably cheer me up. Show this know-it-all that I know what I'm doing.* "You're on."

27

How to be Rich — Chuck Rylant

After a few quick texts with Molly to be sure everything was fine at the shop, David pulled his clubs out of the car, and they headed into the clubhouse to sign in. David had to admit that it was great to be back up there. The pristine club house, the impeccable service from the staff, the perfectly manicured landscaping—it all made David appreciate getting out of the shop.

"Mr. Parson! Hello!" Julio, the club manager, sounded surprised.

David grinned sheepishly. "Yes, it's been a while."

Julio hesitated and started to say something, but then Walter wheeled up with his clubs.

"I finally talked him into a round," Walter said.

"Oh, you're both playing today?" Julio asked, sounding relieved. "Perfect day for it." He waved them through.

Once at the cart, Walter fiddled with his beer cooler. No matter what, he always brought the same beat-up red-and-white cooler with a six-pack of cheap domestic beer.

It was still early enough that the air was brisk, but the sun was beginning to dry the dew that remained in the shade. David took in the scent of freshly cut grass, which was a pleasant break from the exhaust and grease smell that consumed most of his days. He looked across the green at the tall trees and thought how beautiful a day it was and that he should take time off from the shop to enjoy life a little more often.

They bickered over who would drive the cart, and once Walter prevailed, he drove onto the green.

Eleven

Walter lined up a shot, squinting into the sun. As he waggled his hips to get into position, he said, "So you let that woman talk you into her crap."

David had been mentally thinking through his own shot, so he didn't register what Walter meant at first. "What woman?"

"That ad lady."

"Oh, Sharon." David pulled out his driver. "The program just started. It will pay off."

Walter swung, made contact, and sent the ball out over the fairway. "David, that ad's not going to get you anywhere."

Damn, that was a pretty good shot. "Yeah?" David put his own tee down.

"Whatever you spent on that ad was money thrown into the garbage."

David stared out at the flagpole in the distance. With all the money he had spent, that was not what he wanted to hear.

"You're sure you want to use that driver?"

David gripped it more firmly. "Yes, I'm sure." He adjusted his stance over the tee.

"I've made the same mistake, you know," Walter said. "More times than I can count."

"Used this driver?" David asked.

"No, bonehead, that brand advertising nonsense."

"Uh-huh." David concentrated on his shot.

"Brand advertising. It's what you usually see in newspapers, magazines, billboards, and television, and it's what that lady was selling."

David swung, and sent the ball about two thirds as far as Walter had. They both silently watched it land.

"Those ads," Walter continued, "are essentially overpriced business cards. They don't work, at least not for us regular guys."

Irritated, David headed for the cart. "Regular guys?"

Walter followed him and they loaded up their clubs. "Real entrepreneurs—business owners who live and die by the bottom line," Walter said. "We don't have budgets to waste on advertising that doesn't work, nor can we afford advertising that offers no way to measure whether it's working or not."

"Aw, I see those kinds of ads all the time. Why would people do them if they don't work?"

"Because they don't know what they should be doing. Sure, those ads look nice, and they don't hurt necessarily, but they surely don't bring in business in a measurable, consistent way."

David frowned. "I liked it."

"You were supposed to like it," Walter said. "You're the one paying for it. But the only judge who matters is your customer."

David did not know whom to believe, and he was not inclined to believe Walter. Sharon had been very convincing. "So I'm not supposed to promote my business?"

Walter perked up in his seat. "That's a great question!"

David rolled his eyes. *Here it comes.*

Twelve

Walter indeed started to lecture as he drove, more slowly than David thought necessary, over to where the next shot would play.

"These advertising people earn a commission selling ad space," Walter said, "so the more you buy, the more money they make. You want to spend as little as possible while they want to squeeze as much out of you as they can."

David looked at the trees. He was still skeptical as Walter continued his sermon.

"Here's the thing, David. They get paid whether your ad works or not. Big companies can afford to waste buckets of money on image advertising. They need to impress stockholders, board members, and the media. But you can't afford to throw money away like that."

David stayed silent. He wasn't going to admit anything.

"Corporations are giant bureaucracies," Walter said, getting more animated. "Just like government—when politics are involved, common sense goes out the window. Entrepreneurs, on the other hand, need ads that produce income, often before the bad check clears that paid for the advertising."

David noticed that Walter's excitement was growing the more he talked about marketing. Advice, David had heard, was a form of nostalgia, and Walter was indulging himself.

"Entrepreneurs," Walter said, waving a hand in front of him as he drove, "can't wait years before our advertisements deliver. Every small business owner who has tried has gone broke."

David wanted to bring him back down to earth. "If brand advertising doesn't work, why does everyone do it?" he asked.

Walter gave an exasperated groan. "Everyone wants to push the easy button," he said. "When the ad salesman walks in, every business owner wants to write a check and pass off their marketing responsibility. But it doesn't work that way. You have to build a multistep system. Nobody makes their buying decisions the exact moment they give you money. There's an incubation period before most buyers will open their wallets."

Okay, now he's ranting. "Incubation period?" David asked. "What's that got to do with marketing?"

Walter pulled up to the area for the next shot. "Do you remember when I bought my fishing boat?" They pulled out their clubs and set up for the shot.

David laughed. "Yes, you were annoying. It was all you talked about for months."

"Before or after I bought it?"

David squinted. "Before."

Walter set up and swung. David watched as the ball traced a wide arc overhead. *Okay, he's on his game today.* David pulled out his own club and got ready.

"Right, it was before," Walter said. "Almost every shopper goes through that same cycle. Something triggers an idea for a purchase, so they think about it for a while as it simmers. Then they start researching and talking about it with others until they are finally ready to buy. This timeline can be long or short, usually depending on the price of the item."

David botched his shot and the ball skewed left.

Walter clapped him on the back. "Tough luck." They hopped into the cart to chase down their balls.

"You mean if I were buying a pair of jeans I wouldn't research it as long as it took you to buy a boat?" David asked, to get the conversation off his shot.

"Especially not *those* jeans," Walter said.

David side-eyed him.

Walter grinned. "The point almost every business owner misses is that consumers are in the research phase the majority of the time. They're in buying mode for a relatively short window. Yet the majority of advertising is aimed at the people ready to buy that minute."

David had never considered that. He did not want to show it, though. "Your shot," he said.

Walter got into his stance. "Let's assume that eighty percent of the time consumers are in the research mode and in buying mode the other twenty percent. Wouldn't it make sense that some of your advertising should focus on that majority group?"

"Focus on non-buyers? How does that make sense?"

"Well, not all the time. You'll go broke if all you provide is research information to window shoppers. But the front of your marketing system should lure in folks you can later convert to buyers."

That made sense—sort of. "I suppose," David said skeptically.

"Once your front-end advertising attracts quality prospects, you can follow up with them so they can get to know, like, and trust you."

Walter shot again, this time bringing it right into the green near the hole. David's shot went a bit wider.

Walter started in again. "Consumers need to feel safe before they'll invest their money, and that's hard to do with a single brand-style advertisement."

"Look," David said finally. "I just want to focus on the game."

Walter looked like he was about to argue, but the set of David's jaw must have made him change his mind. The conversation from then on stuck strictly to golf.

The game ended with Walter ahead by three strokes. Back at his house when David dropped him off, Walter got out of the car and stood next to the door.

"Before I go," he said, "I have one final question."

David had enjoyed the golf, but he was ready for the afternoon to be over. "What's that?"

"What is your most valuable business asset?"

David's face showed total and irritated confusion.

Walter laughed. "When you figure that out, everything in your business will change."

Thirteen

David stewed over that last question as he drove back to the shop. He could not see the connection between his business assets and marketing, nor could he see how the answer would help him. He thought about it until his phone vibrated in his pocket. David fished it out to see a text message from Jen.

"What do you want me to do about Zack's tuition?" the message read.

A surge of anxiety rushed through David. *She's got to be pissed.* He did not have time to deal with this marketing nonsense. He had a business to run, and he needed to make some money. He had to get out of this hole before he could worry about anything else.

David drove into the shop's parking lot and started trying to answer Jen's text. But Tony, one of his mechanics, came out to him holding a handful of cylinder head bolts in his grease-covered hands.

"Bad news, boss."

"What's up?"

Tony handed one of the bolts to David, who immediately noticed

37

the threads that were packed full of aluminum engine-block material.

"Do they all look like this?"

"Most of them," Tony said.

David became sarcastic. "That's just great." Mrs. Clark was already contemplating buying a new car because of frequent, expensive repairs. This one could get very expe-nsive. David hated asking the customer for more money after the initial estimate, but eating the cost would be even worse.

"It's common with this engine," the mechanic said, "but we can fix it without pulling the motor."

"How?" David asked.

"I found a jig that locks onto the engine block. I can drill and install new thread inserts without pulling the motor," Tony explained.

"Call the tool truck," David said.

"It's only available from the dealership," Tony said reluctantly. "And it's expensive."

David contemplated his options for a moment. The last thing he wanted to do was go crawling to the dealership where he used to work, especially when he realized that most of the profit from this job was beginning to evaporate away. The jig and the extra labor were going to suck up any profit he might have earned from the job.

But Tony needed to have an answer. "If she approves the extra labor," David said, "charge the tool to my dealership house account." He had gotten an account after leaving his job there because some things he could only get there.

David remembered Walter's question about his most valuable business asset. *It's got to be my tools,* he thought, but he could not see how realizing that would offer any help to his business.

Fourteen

Hidden behind the big-box stores was a small, obscure restaurant. Its exterior was subdued compared with the bright signage promoting the rest of the businesses in the shopping center. When David and Jennifer walked in that night, David surveyed the eclectic mix of décor scattered randomly on the walls. After a few minutes, the hostess seated them at the table Jennifer had reserved where they could celebrate their twenty-first wedding anniversary.

David studied the odd menu, which was written in black Sharpie marker on a slate of wood. The place was loud and packed with customers throwing peanut shells on the floor. David looked down at the floor, then glanced at Jennifer with a confused look on his face.

"Don't worry," Jennifer said. "It's really good. I was here with a girl-friend a couple months ago. One night when you worked late."

The waiter took their order as Jennifer asked about David's day. He was still kind of distracted by what Walter had said and did not really want to tell her he had been out golfing.

"How did you find this place?" David asked instead. His mind wandered as he looked around the strange restaurant. He was curious how this mom-and-pop joint was still afloat. The chains were absorbing the little guys, but this little place was defying the odds.

"A few months ago the restaurant sent me an offer for two free meals," Jennifer said. "Stacy loved it. And they sent a promotion last week when we were planning our anniversary."

David looked around at all the tables full of customers. He wanted his shop to have the same energy—only with cars and mechanics instead of diners and waiters. "What do you think my most valuable business asset is?" he blurted out.

"What?"

"Something Walter said. He asked what I thought my most valuable business asset was."

Jennifer paused to think about it. She had been around large corporations for years. "Your employees?" she asked.

"That's a good one. Today I needed an important tool for a cylinder head job, so I was wondering if it's my tools."

"What did Walter say it was?"

David went back to his menu. "He wanted me to figure it out."

Jen suddenly cleared her throat. "Uh-oh."

David looked to where she was indicating with her head. It was Frank, staggering toward them. David stiffened. Frank was about the last person he wanted to see.

Fifteen

Frank wove a bit unsteadily on his feet toward their table from the restaurant's bar.

Great, David thought. *Seven o'clock and he's already drunk.*

Working for Frank was one reason David no longer touched the stuff. Frank owned the franchise for a neglected car dealership, the one David had to order parts from, in fact. Once upon a time Frank had been very successful, but he had run the repair side of the business into the ground while car sales limped along. He survived by cutting corners in the worst ways and nabbing an occasional customer via the big manufacturers he was still certified to repair and sell for. Frank had driven most of his employees away, including David.

"Davey!" Frank called. "You're looking good." He burped a little out of the side of his mouth.

"Thanks." David pointedly turned back toward his menu, hoping Frank would get the hint.

The waitress arrived at the table to take their order a moment after

Frank did. As she tried to guide them through the menu, Frank continued talking at them in his slurred voice.

"How's that little shop of yours doing?" Frank asked, emphasizing the word *little*. "I got a call from one of your guys today for a cylinder head jig."

David gritted his teeth. "We're doing fine."

"When you're done playing around, you can always come back and work for me."

My personal nightmare. "No, thanks," David said.

Frank, an old Navy man, raised his right hand to his forehead and saluted before he turned and staggered toward the door.

"Appetizer?" the waitress asked helpfully.

"I'll have the roasted artichoke," David said, pointing at the menu. His hand trembled, partly from anger, but mostly from fear that Frank's offer might become a reality someday.

Sixteen

The following morning, David was greeted with a sharp breeze blowing the marine layer off the coast. He enjoyed the warm weather, but hearing Tony's air ratchet in the garage reenergized him more than the spring weather.

Mrs. Clark had approved the cylinder head repair before David arrived at the shop. Tony had finished the brakes on Elaine's BMW yesterday, while David and Walter were at the golf course, but during a test drive, Tony noticed the slipping transmission. David conferred with Elaine, who had approved the new clutch. He had already started pulling the transmission before Walter arrived for his morning coffee.

David planned to work all day to finish her car and figured that Tony should finish Mrs. Clark's Mercedes by the end of the following day. Walter's job had turned out to be pretty big, so that would be a huge help. With those two big jobs finished, David would put a dent in Zack's tuition payment.

Walter arrived predictably at nine for his first cup of coffee and strolled over to David, who was standing underneath his wife's raised BMW. David explained the work order he had already gone over with Elaine the day before.

"I brought it in for a checkup and now it needs a clutch? What kind of shop are you running here?" Walter asked grinning, while hazing David.

"Why didn't you bring it in sooner?" David asked, but he grinned back.

"I don't drive this car," Walter said. "But I did notice the transmission slipping a bit when I drove Elaine to Carmel."

"You drove the BMW there like this?" David asked. "That's a three-hour drive!"

"Elaine never pays attention to that stuff," Walter said. "If the red warning light flashed, she would just drive home faster."

"C'mon, Walter," David said, defending Elaine. She was a nice lady.

"Send us a reminder next time."

"Molly has a new estimate for you in the office," David said, "but I've already started on the clutch."

"Just get it done because I'm Elaine's taxi until she gets her car back." Walter said. He hovered for a moment, dragged a metal stool across the concrete shop floor and was about to sit down when David interrupted him.

"See that sign, Walter?" David asked.

It was the same sign that was posted in every mechanic shop as a joke, but the message was clear.

Labor Rates

$55 per hour

$65 if you watch

$75 if you give advice

$85 if you help

"Ha! That's not the kind of advice I'll be giving." Walter slurped his coffee. "Did you figure out your most valuable business asset?"

"Oh, yeah," David said, more confidently than he felt. "It's my tools."

"Not exactly."

David tried Jennifer's answer. "My employees, then?"

"Your most valuable asset," Walter said, "is your list."

"My list? My list of what?"

"Customers and prospects."

David set his ratchet on top of the toolbox to fish for a wrench. "Huh?"

"When you have a quality list of customers or prospects, you can send them promotions any time you need money," Walter said. "It's like an ATM machine."

That caught David's attention, but he pretended to be intent on his repair.

"Most business owners ignore the low-hanging fruit in their business," Walter said. "Rarely, if ever, do they follow up with customers they've already worked with. But those folks are far more likely to buy from you than a new prospect."

"I thought I was supposed to get new prospects."

"Right. It all works together."

David shrugged. He was mystified.

"Everyone wants their past customers to return, but they focus their marketing solely on new-customer acquisition. The advertising salespeople love that. It's more profitable for the ad salesmen to sell brand advertising targeting new prospects, even though following up with past customers is usually more profitable."

David was listening. Sharon never said anything like what Walter was explaining.

"How often do you contact your customers, David?" Walter asked.

"Um, every time they come in, I guess," David said, a little embarrassed.

"Yeah, that's called 'hope and pray' marketing. Everyone does it. They wait around wishing someone would come in rather than following up to drive them into the shop."

Walter's bluntness was painful. "Who's got time for that?" David asked.

"You need to make the time. A lot of people are using the internet, but the telephone and mail still work."

"So I have to do three things for each customer?"

"Depends on the customer," Walter answered. "For me and Elaine, a postcard would be best, but other people are into email, texts, or even that social media thing."

"I would think it would be annoying to hear from me all the time," David said. He was not ready to admit that some of what Walter said made sense.

"That depends. There are two reasons to contact someone: to build trust or to present offers. People want to do business with those they know, like, and trust, and we've all been scammed, so we rarely trust anyone who is selling something. Trust does not come by chance, so you have to add rapport-building components into your marketing."

"My customers already trust me."

"I'm sure they do, but you're in a dating relationship with your customers," Walter said. "If you don't give them attention, someone one else will."

David stuck out his jaw. He had never once reached out to his customers—it had never occurred to him. He was trying to grow his business, not lose the customers he already had.

"If you only contact your customers when you are selling, eventually they will tune you out. They need to look forward to hearing from you," Walter said.

"Look forward to a sales message? Who would do that?"

"You craft a valuable message—not that branding stuff," Walter said. "You can build trust with friendly and informative follow-up communication. Think about it like this. Most people are disappointed when they open their mail and find the usual pile of bills, but when you get the rare birthday card or personal letter, it's a different feeling."

"It's usually the first piece of the pile I open," David said.

"Exactly," Walter said. "That's how you want your customers to feel when they hear from you. The more personal and helpful you are in your follow-up messages, the more they will want to hear from you. Like a lady would when she hears from Mr. Right after a great first date."

"You want me to send my customers cards?" David asked with skepticism. It sounded a little odd for a repair shop.

"Birthday cards are a nice touch," Walter said. "Personal newsletters, postcards from your vacations, and other personal correspondence will help you build the relationship with your customers."

"Really." It sounded kind of fake to David.

"That's just the beginning," Walter said. "If you only send personal correspondence, your customers will like you, but it will not establish you as the expert in your field. To build trust, you must also demonstrate your expertise with tips, articles, and other helpful resources that position you as a consumer advocate instead of a salesman."

"Before, you also said something about offers?" David asked.

"Ah, you were paying attention!" Walter chuckled. "At some point in your marketing system, you have to offer your services. The more offers you send, the more money you'll earn."

"Still seems kind of pushy."

"Not if it's useful to your customers. Contact them and tell them about a new product, service, or sale. How will they know otherwise?"

David thought about how much time all this would take, and he shook his head. He had never dated more than one person at a time before. "I don't have time for all of this. I've got a business to run."

Walter shrugged. "It's up to you, David. You can keep wasting time doing things that won't work, or you can learn how to get customers."

Seventeen

By Monday, things were looking a little better, at least financially. Tony finished the big cylinder head job, and David wrapped up Walter's transmission and brakes. Completing two big jobs gave David a shot of motivation.

However, later that day, David's cell phone rang. He looked at the phone screen and instantly got a knot in his stomach.

"Zack," David said into his phone.

"Are you busy, Dad?"

"No, no. I've been meaning to call you—"

"Me first," Zack interrupted. "I'm thinking about taking a break from school."

David heard his son fire those words out superfast as though wanting to spare him the blow. He replied heavily, "It's about your tuition."

"No, that's not it," Zack said, but David knew he was not being entirely truthful. "I need more experience anyway. I can take some time off to help out at the shop."

"Worry about your classes, Zack," David said. "I'll get the money together."

"I can always go back later," Zack said.

"Trust me, that's harder than it sounds." David knew from experience. He had always wanted to go to college, but life always seemed to get in the way.

After they hung up, David had to go pick up Walter's wife, Elaine. Her car was ready. He wanted to help her out and ensure he would be paid sooner. As David got up from his desk to get going, the phone rang again.

It was Jennifer. After a few moments, even Molly, from her seat at the other end of the room, could hear that Jen was upset

"Zack just called me! He was turned away from registering for classes!" Jen shouted.

David rubbed his eyes.

"His tuition account was empty!"

"We finished two jobs today—" David started, before he was cut off.

"You promised you would fund Zack's school account!"

"I'm working on it!"

"I've heard it before, David," Jennifer said. "Payroll is due again too. Agh!" Her aggravation came out in an annoyed outburst. "Just—we'll talk about it later." She hung up.

David slammed down his phone. He was not mad at his wife; she had every right to be frustrated. He felt he had let her—and everyone—down.

It was time for David to admit to himself that he was further behind than he thought. That new ad was supposed to solve this tuition problem, but instead the expense made things worse. After buying the expensive tool, there would not be much left for Zack. David was deeper in the hole than before he started experimenting with advertising.

David was tired. Maybe that job with Frank was not as bad as he remembered. Then he shook his head. No way.

He raised his eyes to see Molly looking at him sympathetically.

"I'm headed to Elaine's," he said shortly as he left.

Eighteen

David drove Elaine's car to the house she and Walter had in a nice part of town. As he walked up the steps of the raised foundation, he paused next to the rocking chair on the front porch and admired the perfectly manicured lawn and rose garden. It was an older home, probably built in the 1950s, but still immaculate.

"It's so nice to see you, David. Please come in," Elaine said as she opened the squeaky front screen door.

"Your car is ready," David said. "It's in good shape now."

"I'm sure it is."

"I'm sorry it took a little longer than expected."

"Don't worry about that," Elaine said, smiling at David as she dismissed any talk about her car. "I'm sure Walter complained, but we got along fine with Walter's truck." She flipped open their front-door mailbox and shuffled through the envelopes.

"Is he around?"

"Oh, he's making his rounds, I suppose," Elaine said. "Ever since he retired he's always looking for something to keep himself busy. Come on in while I grab my things."

The house inside was beautifully appointed, almost Victorian. David laughed to himself when he thought how true it must be that opposites attract. Elaine was all class. He wondered about Walter's background. He knew Walter used to own a business of some kind, but he did not know much else. By the looks of their house, he had done very well.

"I hope I'm not keeping you too long," Elaine said. She was assembling the mysterious things ladies assemble as they get ready to leave the house.

"Not at all," David said. He looked around. "You have a lovely place. What did Walter do before he retired?"

"What didn't Walter do!" Elaine said. "You know, he never went to college, but he worked hard. He loves business. At one point I counted that we had owned fourteen different businesses. There was the cabinet shop, the roofing company, the insurance firm—now I can't remember all of them. I talked him into a flower shop for a couple of years."

"He must have done pretty well?" David had not had any idea of the extent of Walter's business background.

"Well, not always," Elaine said. "It was tough in the early days, believe me. Many of those businesses struggled. Some of them failed. But as time passed, each new one did a little better than the last. I think Walter learned a lot through the years, especially the early years when things weren't going very well."

This was all news to David. He began to wonder if maybe he should pay Walter more attention.

Eighteen

"Ready to go?" Elaine asked.

It's always the one who delays the leaving who asks that. "Whenever you are."

"Let me grab my checkbook," Elaine said. "And maybe we can avoid letting things go as much as we did this time." She picked up a card from her mail. "Maybe you could do something like this?"

"What is that?" David asked as he reached for it.

"My dentist sends us these postcards every six months."

It was a reminder card for her next cleaning. David read the postcard and hesitated. "Uh, maybe." He did not understand why she was referring to a dentist's postcard.

"Walter used to have boxes of junk mail all over the house," Elaine said. "He was always looking for promotional ideas to send customers. When I had the flower shop he taught me a little about marketing."

David's face must have conveyed his confusion.

"I always forget to bring my car in," Elaine explained. "It would be nice if you sent me a reminder like the dentist does."

Huh, thought David.

Nineteen

David woke up in the middle of the night, which had become a regular occurrence. He tried to dismiss it and go back to sleep, but Elaine's postcard kept nagging at him. It must have been germinating in his subconscious all night.

David glanced at the clock: 3:27 a.m. It would be a long and exhausting day. David squirmed and readjusted the sheets until Jennifer started mumbling something he could not understand. David's stress was affecting his wife.

All of a sudden it clicked. After a few minutes' contemplation, the idea seemed ridiculously simple. David climbed out of bed, got dressed, and drove to the shop.

He was the only car on the road except for a cop and a guy delivering newspapers. By the time he got to the shop, it was still dark and well before business hours. He had time to work without interruptions.

David's first hurdle was gathering his customer's contact information. He remembered what Walter had said about the list being his most important asset. David had never organized his customers into a list before, but he hoped the computer had that information. Two years earlier, David had purchased software to simplify writing estimates. He remembered the computer program prompted for customer mailing addresses, which David and Molly dutifully entered for no other reason than because the computer asked for them.

It took David about an hour, but he eventually found a way to generate a list of his past customers and their mailing addresses. This was exactly what David was looking for. Now he was even more optimistic that this new idea was going to work.

When Elaine mentioned the postcard, David initially was not sure what to do about it. But as it percolated in his brain, he realized he could copy it almost word for word. David did not have a creative bone in his body, but he decided if he replaced words like "teeth" with "oil change," it was almost a perfect match. David would have never thought a marketing piece for a dentist could be an almost perfect match for an auto repair shop.

"It's time for your..." David muttered to himself as he tried to figure out what to swap for "annual cleaning." "...3,000-mile oil change." That would work fine. David grinned as he realized the smiling-tooth image probably would not work. He found a car cartoon image on the internet.

David was pleased with himself. While he was not remotely computer-savvy, it only took him about an hour to create a postcard. This was the first marketing piece he ever done. It was easier than he thought.

Twenty

At home after a long day, David set the stack of postcards down on the kitchen table. He almost felt like a teenager asking someone on a first date. Then he laughed, remembering how Walter had said marketing was like dating. He could relate.

He had stopped at a print shop to get copies made on postcard material, and he was ready to work with his customer list in hand. He settled down with a pen and stamps even before getting a snack.

Jennifer walked in from work a little later and set her bags down on the dining room table. "What's all this, David?"

David kept writing. "This is Zack's tuition."

"What do you mean?" Jennifer asked. "Is this Walter's idea?"

"No, it's mine."

"Really?"

"Well, not exactly," David said. "I copied it from a dentist postcard that Walter's wife gave me."

Jen picked up a card and squinted at it. "You're going to mail these to your customers like this?" That was her polite way of saying they looked homemade.

"I don't have time to make them fancy," David said. "I figure doing something is better than sitting around and doing nothing."

"This is for an oil change," Jen said. "How's that going to bring in much money?"

David had already done the math. Even though his list was so small that even if they all came in it would not be very much money, but he still had high hopes.

"I need a couple of big jobs to catch up," David said. "If ten people come in for an oil change, maybe two of them will also need major repairs. Can you help me?"

"Why don't you have Molly address those?" Jennifer asked.

"It won't take long," David said. "I just want to get it done."

"All right, let me just get a glass of wine."

They sat at the kitchen table and hand addressed each postcard. It did not take as long as they thought, and soon David wrapped them up and headed for the post office to place them in the night drop and begin the wait to see if they would work.

Twenty-One

David did not tell anyone what he had done with the postcards, but he kept pestering Molly about whether anyone they had not seen in a while had come in. As she kept saying, "No," he started to get depressed.

A few days after he had sent the cards, Walter walked in to get his coffee. David was sitting in his office staring blankly ahead. What would he do if the cards did not work out? He had no idea.

Walter came over to David's desk and cleared his throat. He pulled one of the postcards out of his pocket.

Oh, yeah, we even sent one to Walter! But David did not feel up to Walter's banter today.

"I already know," David said, preempting the blow.

"You know what?" Walter asked.

"They don't look very professional. I made it myself."

"That doesn't matter," Walter said. "How well did it work?"

"It hasn't worked at all—yet. Maybe mail doesn't work any better than the newspaper." David said, frustrated.

"This is a lot better than your other advertising," Walter said as he looked at the postcard. "It's a great start. Don't blame the medium."

A compliment! David perked up a little. "Medium?"

"The medium is how you deliver your message," Walter said. "You said mail and the newspaper don't work. Any medium can work if you use it to deliver the right message to the right people. You can't dismiss the medium when you don't have the right message."

"Is there something wrong with my message?" David asked with more frustration.

"It's close, but you could do more. The postcard is delivering your message. The message is your offer, which I'm really glad to see you are doing. The medium is the postcard, delivered by the post office. In this case, I don't think there is a problem with the medium. Your message is close, but your offer is missing one of the three critical components."

"All right, enlighten me." David said. He was a little annoyed, but glad he had been close at least. Two out of three was not bad.

"Every offer needs three attributes," Walter said. "Let me write them down. It will make more sense."

Walter reached for a piece of paper and wrote the following:

1. Specific

2.

3.

"You have a specific reason for your offer—their car is due for an oil change," Walter continued. "That's perfect. Do you see the difference from the brand advertisement you ran in the newspaper? Those ads were big business cards that said nothing. In contrast, this offer is for something specific. You're offering a discounted oil change."

Okay, that makes sense. "What's number two?"

Walter adjusted the paper on the desk and wrote the next one on the list.

1. Specific
2. Call to action
3.

"Your call to action says to bring the postcard into the store. That's fine." Walter said.

"Well, what else could it be?" David asked.

"It could be pick up the phone, visit the store, order now, or anything where you can track the results of your offer," Walter said. "But the call to action must be clear and easy for your customer. Don't make your customer figure it out. If they bring in the card, you know whether the card worked or not and you can measure those results. If no one brings in the card, you know it didn't work."

Don't remind me. David became glum again. "That's about the size of it."

Just then, the door jingled. The mail carrier came in and instead of leaving the mail on the counter, he looked around for help.

"What's up?" David asked.

"I need a signature."

"Is this about the postcards?"

"I don't know. It's probably your lottery check," the carrier said.

But as David took the envelope and signed for it, he knew that good news never comes by certified mail. David opened the letter as the mail carrier left and immediately felt a huge knot in his stomach.

Twenty-Two

The letter was about the lease on the lifts. David took a deep breath. They made it sound like repossession could happen any minute now.

David was still staring at the letter when Walter asked gruffly, "Can we get on with our lesson?"

"Uh, sure," David said, shoving the letter under a form on a clipboard.

Walter grunted. David could not tell whether Walter knew the letter was bad news. But he also remembered what Elaine had said about all their businesses. Walter had even failed at some. "So yeah, what's the third thing?"

"One more thing," Walter said. He grabbed the paper again and completed the list.

1. Reason
2. Call to action
3. Scarcity

David laughed ruefully. "The only scarcity I've got is customers."

Walter shook his head. "You can change that."

"With this system of yours?"

"Just bear with me," Walter said. "That's the problem with your offer—it didn't have scarcity. That's probably why it had such a poor response."

"But it's a great deal on an oil change," David challenged. "Why wouldn't they jump on it?"

"Because they open their mail while cooking dinner," Walter said, "or as they're racing out to grab the kids from school. They may think your postcard was a good idea until they set it down to deal with their crying baby."

David nodded his head, but his thoughts wandered back to the repossession letter.

"Like now, when you should be listening to me. You're distracted."

"Huh?" David snapped his attention back to Walter. "Right. Continue."

"There is a lot fighting for your customers' attention," Walter continued. "They may genuinely want what you're offering but still not make the call. You have to create a reason for them to act now, before they get distracted."

"Pay up or else," David said, still obsessing over that letter.

"Sure, but not so threatening. But yeah, get an oil change or else."

"Or else what?" David said.

"They'll miss it."

David rolled his eyes. "Miss what?"

"The deal. Think about diamonds."

Diamonds were about the last thing David wanted to think about—he had never been able to afford them.

"The thing about people," Walter went on, "is that we want what we cannot have. Everyone thinks diamonds are such a big deal, right? But really, diamonds have no inherent value. They are incredibly expensive only because some profiteer back in the old days decided to market these little sparkly things as rare. Supply was actually limited to create demand."

David was surprised enough to focus fully on what Walter was saying. "Really?"

"Yes. The entire diamond industry understands this. When you understand what creates the demand for diamonds, you can apply the same principles to your marketing," Walter replied. "Look how those fancy nightclubs create value out of thin air by roping off a corner with a big bouncer to keep people out. As soon as they label it 'VIP,' everyone wants to go into an area that previously had no value."

Okay, I get that. "But how does that apply to my business?"

"Every offer you make must include a deadline or limited supply," Walter said.

David frowned. "But people can have as many oil changes as they want."

"Not according to you."

"I just fabricate scarcity of oil changes?" David asked.

"Well, it can't look unreasonable," Walter answered. "When you create arbitrary deadlines, consumers will see through them. If you're smart, you will include a credible reason why the offer has a deadline or limited supply. If your customers do not believe your offer, they will ignore it."

"Like those 'fifty percent off,' department store offers?" David asked. "My immediate thought is that it's always fifty percent off."

"Exactly," Walter said. "The more you can rationalize your offer, the more seriously your customers will take it."

"If I use a deadline, when should it expire?" David asked.

"The sooner the offer expires, the more urgent it becomes."

David was quiet for a moment as he pondered Walter's advice. "I guess I can wait a few months and try it again."

"That's nonsense!" Walter insisted. "Make another postcard and send it today."

"But I just mailed it Monday," David said. "I don't want to be a pest."

"Your customers need their oil changed," Walter said. "You're helping them save money on something they need. How's that being a pest?"

"Maybe," David said.

"Use the same card, but add a sentence that you're following up because you did not hear from them. You wanted to let them know the offer ends, say, three or four days after you're sending the card. Don't make it complicated. Just get it in the mail."

David nodded slowly.

"And another thing. Are you sure you have the complete list?"

Twenty-Three

"The complete list?" David's head spun. "I think so."

But Walter was already headed to the lobby, motioning for David to follow. Molly looked up at them expectantly from the counter.

"Molly," Walter said, "David sent out a postcard this week."

Molly looked surprised. "You did? What did it say?"

Walter waved this off. "Who did you send it to, David?"

"Here." David pulled up the list he had created on the computer. Molly squinted down it.

"Molly," asked Walter, "is that everyone? Every customer you've ever had?"

"Well, there's more in the paper files in the closet. And maybe some more in the attic."

Walter raised his eyebrows and looked at David.

David groaned. "We have to go back through all of that?"

"Otherwise, you're leaving money on the table," Walter said.

Thus began the afternoon project. Once Walter left, David dug though old file boxes looking for customer names and addresses. The boxes were a mess. The information was written in old notebooks and even scraps of paper. Digging through the files was wildly tedious. When David first opened the business, he had no employees and organization was not his strong suit. He was the only one who knew where to look, and now he realized what a colossal mistake it was not maintaining a customer database from the beginning.

But every time David came up with a new batch of names, Molly would let her fingers fly entering them into the database. The list got longer and longer.

When Jennifer called to check in that afternoon, David let her know what was up and that he would be working late. Once he had closed his office door so Molly would not overhear, he even swallowed his pride and told her about the repo letter. To her credit, she did not yell. So he yelled at himself.

"I haven't even made enough to pay for our son's college tuition, and now this?" David asked. "I think it's time to start being realistic. I may need to find a job."

Jennifer knew he was doing his best. "We're going through a tough spot. But don't give up, David."

"I can't run my shop without those car lifts," David said. "We use them all day. That's how we get underneath the cars."

"What can I do to help?" Jennifer asked.

David shared what Walter had told him today about the postcards, but as he talked with Jennifer, he began to feel he was just going through the motions. He was not enthused about spending more time and money on another batch of postcards, especially after the last round was so disappointing.

Just before they hung up, she said, "Well, you have until the end of the month at least. It's worth it to try this one last thing."

David resigned himself to a long evening alone at the shop when Molly left for the day, but he was in for a surprise—his wife really came through.

Twenty-Four

Jennifer showed up to keep him company, and then she took over like the pro she was. She was organized and comfortable taking charge of these types of jobs. Managing teams of people was what she did in her role as a project manager at an engineering firm.

She had done some shopping for supplies, too, on the way over. She edited the postcard with a deadline, printed them right there in the shop on card stock, and set David to work cutting them down to size. This saved printing costs. She made one card for those customers who had received David's prior cards, and one for those who were new to the list. She even printed the addresses directly onto the cards, so all they would have to do was stamp them.

David had already purchased more rolls of stamps. It was about eight o'clock by the time the two of them had finished printing, addressing, and stamping. The result was several tightly rubber-banded bundles of stamped postcards addressed to each of his past customers.

"Phew!" Jennifer said, brushing her bangs from her forehead. "We're done!"

David smiled. She had never looked prettier. "How about I take my girl out to dinner?"

"Please!" Then she winced, jokingly. "We can just about afford an elegant fast-food drive-through."

He laughed. "That sounds perfect."

They drove by the post office on the way and dropped the bundles in the overnight mail drop box. David was getting used to the waiting game, wondering if his latest marketing campaign would have an impact. Only time would tell.

Twenty-Five

David did not even have time to get worried before one of his former customers walked in holding a postcard just two days later. Mrs. Reynolds had not been in for a couple of years. When she walked in holding his postcard, David's eyes lit up as if she was a relative who he thought had been lost at sea.

"Mrs. Reynolds! How great to see you! You're looking well." He gave her a huge smile in greeting. Creating the list had reminded him of all the clients he'd had, and he had always been good with matching names to faces.

She laughed. "Thanks, David! You know, I'd never considered using you for oil changes. I've been going to one of those quick lubes. I'd much rather come here, though."

They did her oil change right away. After she left, David picked up the phone and called Jen. "Those postcards are working! An old customer just walked in with one."

"That's great, David," Jennifer said. "Did you sell her any other work besides the oil change?"

"No," David said. "Her car was in good shape, but we might be onto something."

"While I have you, I need to ask…" Jennifer hesitated.

"What?" David asked with concern.

"We're still behind on payroll," Jennifer said. "I don't have the money. What do you want me to do?"

David was quiet. He had to pay his employees. There was no way he could put that off any longer. "Friday is the deadline on that postcard. That gives us a couple of days. Let's see if something more comes out of it."

"I'm sorry, David. I wish I wasn't delivering bad news. I just don't know what to do."

David was hopeful about the postcard, but so far he had spent more on postage than it had brought in with one oil change. He needed something—anything.

Twenty-Six

On Friday morning, David got into the shop a little late. The shop was already open and Molly was helping two customers in the lobby. Walter was sitting in David's office chair nursing his coffee.

"That's my chair, old man," David said.

"You might learn something if you show your elders some respect," Walter said.

"What are you two squabbling about today?" Molly asked as she wrapped up with two service orders. She pivoted in her chair and looked at them.

"I haven't seen those two for a long time," David said referring to the two customers who had just walked out the door.

Molly held a postcard in each hand. "They both came in with these!"

"Really?" David said as a grin formed on his face.

"One of them was due for a timing-belt service and the other ordered more repairs while she was here," Molly said.

Other customers came in throughout the day. When they closed for the evening, David went home tired, but excited. A total of five past customers came in with the postcard and three of them needed major repairs.

It ended up being a late evening, but David was in a good mood when he opened the door to his house. He was excited to tell Jennifer how well the postcard worked. It was not going to solve all their problems, but at least they could make payroll and she would be pleased about that.

David walked in and was surprised at who he saw sitting at the kitchen table.

Twenty-Seven

Jennifer was standing over the stove when David walked in the kitchen and saw Zack.

Zack got up for a hug. "Hey, Dad."

"What are you doing here?" David said to Zack, but he looked in concern at Jennifer's back, which was firmly turned toward him. Zack's school was three hours away. David did not remember hearing that his son was coming home.

"He's taking this quarter off," Jennifer answered tersely.

"What do you mean?" David asked. The tension in the room was obvious.

"We missed the deadline for his tuition," Jennifer said. Now her accusing eyes were turned toward David.

Zack's eyes went from one of them to the other. "But it's okay, Dad. I can use a little break anyway. And I can do some work around the shop to help out."

Zack's positive attitude made David feel even worse. Not only was David failing in business, but now he was failing as a father.

How to be Rich — Chuck Rylant

David walked up to his son and put a hand on his shoulder. "I'm glad to see you, Zack, but I will fix this. I promise."

Twenty-Eight

David was able to distract himself by spending the weekend catching up with Zack. He kept himself busy at the beginning of the week by working on cars.

The postcard had worked. It had brought in enough work to keep the shop humming for most of the week. They were busy, at least for the moment. David had been able to cover payroll for two weeks. But the clock was ticking on the lift payment.

At least, David thought, *with Zack home, I don't have to worry about tuition.* Then he kicked himself for even thinking that. Zack, though, was cheerful about it and spent hours each day on the shop computer devising who knew what.

David had been a mechanic for so long that he remembered the old days when he would get bored with working on cars all day. But these days, he looked forward to a break from customers, bills, and credit collectors. Turning wrenches had become his therapy.

Most of the new repair work was caught up after a few days, and

David was already worrying what he would do when this stream dried up. He had to figure out his next step.

Walter walked in just before noon the next week and found David standing underneath a car that was raised on one of the shop's lifts. Oil was pouring from the motor into the catch basin sitting beneath.

"Ready for lunch, David?"

"I forgot we had plans." David's hands and arms were covered in grease. He'd been working since six that morning and had not taken a break. "Let me clean up."

"You've been busy," Walter said.

"It's been a good week."

"Let's eat at the club," Walter suggested.

"Sounds good," David said. "I haven't been up there since we were there last time." David washed his hands, took his coveralls off, and walked with Walter to the parking lot. "How about we take the Porsche? I've got to feel her out."

Walter opened the passenger door, but there was nowhere to sit. Electronic monitors covered the seat with wires attached somewhere under the dash; the inside of the car looked like a hospital room. David pushed them aside to make room for Walter.

"Isn't this Raymond's car from the club?" Walter asked.

"Yeah, it is. He left it with me for a while. He won't mind if you come along."

"Beautiful car, but it must have been built for a damn midget," Walter said as he struggled to get into the seat. "I'm getting too old for these little sports cars."

They pulled away from the shop and onto the freeway on-ramp. David downshifted one gear and floored the accelerator. The car squatted and the engine roared to life as the red sports car leaned into the swooping curve of the ramp. The tachometer jumped to 6,000 RPM as they were jerked back into their seats.

"Are you trying to kill us?" Walter asked after they settled into freeway traffic.

"The engine has an intermittent miss when it accelerates. I've been driving the car all week trying to replicate the problem with my monitors connected."

"All these damn computers...they don't make cars like they used to. In my day when we popped the hood there was an engine."

"The basics haven't changed, Walter. This car runs on the same principle as that World War II lawn mower you still use on the weekends." David put his foot on the gas again to pass the car in front of him.

"This is one fast lawn mower," Walter said laughing.

"I think it's Raymond's midlife crisis," David said.

"Does anyone else from the club bring business to your shop?"

"The club has been helpful, but it's hit or miss. The more I'm there, the more business I get, but it takes a lot of time to get a new customer by hanging around the club."

"Networking is unpredictable," Walter said. "You waste a lot of time meeting people who are not your ideal customers. There are more efficient ways to grow a business. Which reminds me—I need to explain the next part of my marketing system."

"There's more?" David laughed. "I think I've got it figured out. Last week was a good one."

David pulled off the freeway and downshifted. The engine revved as he released the clutch, and the car decelerated down the off-ramp toward the club.

Twenty-Nine

They walked through the lobby of the club toward the restaurant.

"Excuse me, Mr. Parson," said someone timidly from behind David.

David heard the voice and looked over his shoulder. Julio hovered there, discreetly. Walter must have sensed the urgency because he stopped too.

"What's up, Julio?" David asked.

"Can I have a word with you, please, sir?"

"Sure, what do you need?" David asked.

"In private, sir?" Julio asked as he looked uncomfortably at Walter.

"Um, okay, I guess."

Julio escorted David back to the pro shop. "I'm sorry, sir. We can't let you play today," Julio explained. He was obviously uncomfortable with the conversation.

"Did we forget a payment or something?" David asked, assuming Jennifer must have made a simple mistake. "We're only here for lunch, but I don't understand. I've been a member for years. It's a simple oversight."

"Actually, sir, you haven't paid in four months, and we've sent you several letters."

David was speechless. He dropped his shoulders and looked at the ground as he wondered how this was possible. "I'm sorry, Julio. I don't know what happened. I'll check with my wife."

"Shall I write you in as Walter's guest if you want to have lunch?" Julio asked in an obvious attempt to smooth over an awkward conversation.

David was flustered. He wasn't sure what to say to Walter. He wanted to leave, but he was stuck.

Thirty

David and Walter sat in the club's restaurant eating lunch on the balcony that overlooked the golf course. David stared at the acres of green, tuning out as Walter rambled on.

David thought about his golf dues. *How could we be four months behind?* He wondered what the rest of their finances looked like. *I should have been more involved with the bills,* he thought.

Maybe the eight-to-five grind at the dealership with Frank was not as bad as he remembered. David was losing hope. Carrying the weight of his business responsibilities made him want to just let the business go, but what would he do with his employees if he closed the doors? He was responsible for the jobs of three other people—each with a family to feed.

"Are you listening, David?" Walter asked.

Walter had been talking about fishing or something. David had been too preoccupied to hear him. Before he could reply, his cell phone started ringing. The shop number was displayed on the screen. It was probably Molly with another routine question.

"I would love just one minute without worrying about the shop," David muttered, but loud enough that Walter overheard. David hit the red end-call button without answering. "What did you say?" he asked Walter.

"I was talking about bait."

The phone started ringing again. It was the shop again. What could possibly be so important? David started to worry, so he picked up the phone.

Thirty-One

When David finally answered, Molly frantically burst out about two burly men who were standing there at Parson's Auto with tools to unbolt the car lifts and haul them away in their large utility truck.

Walter overheard enough of the conversation to offer that it was probably a scare tactic. He said they would need a court order to enter his shop. David's mind went into overdrive. Court orders? Lawsuits? How would he handle that? But he relayed Walter's comment to Molly. She was too rattled to confront the men. She said they had official-looking paperwork and they were intimidating.

"It's not the end of the month yet!" David blurted.

"I don't know why they're here. What should I do?" Molly did not like confrontation.

"I'll take care of it."

David got up from the table in a frenzy, frantically finding the phone number for the collection company and placing the call. He spent the next ten minutes pleading with the account agent, who finally caved in and gave David a thirty-day extension to make his next payment.

When David hung up the phone, he found Walter hovering beside him holding two plastic bags with food containers.

"Got the stuff to go," Walter said. "You seemed busy."

David glanced around the restaurant and wondered how many of the other diners had overheard his conversation. Most people were politely ignoring them and eating, but one or two sets of eyes were looking at him curiously. He was mortified.

"I'm sorry," he said to Walter.

"That's fine. I know exactly what you're going through." Walter said all this at a fast clip, as though he did not really know what to say.

But David took it the wrong way. "Yeah, you just know everything, don't you? Mr. Successful Business Man. While here I am just scraping by—" David stopped himself when he registered Walter's frown. "Look, I've got to get back."

"Sure, sure," Walter said. He handed David his leftovers. "Look, this seems like a bad time. I'll hop a ride back to my place with someone else."

David was so fixated by his problems that he took this for what it was—a way out. "Great. I'll keep you posted about Elaine's car."

"Don't worry about it."

Thirty-Two

As he drove away from the club, David ground and ground through his angry thoughts like a manual transmission refusing to shift into gear.

How did Jennifer let the bills get so far behind? Why didn't she tell me?

As he drove he kept trying to call her with his cell, but she did not answer. The more times he called, the more irrational he became.

The off-ramp to her office was in three exits, then in two. When he came to her exit, he spun the wheel at the last moment and gunned his way to her workplace. He parked in a reserved parking spot and stormed into the building.

"Hi, David!" called the receptionist, but he just stormed past. He went straight for Jen's office, where he pushed the door open so hard that it made a hollow bang as it smacked the wall.

"David! What are you doing here?" Jennifer asked as she was startled away from her computer screen.

"You really screwed me over!" David snapped.

"What?" Jennifer asked with no idea what David was talking about.

"At the club. Julio said you haven't paid our dues in four months," David said. "These people are my customers, Jen. I was humiliated!"

Jen stammered. "You went up there today? I meant to tell you—I didn't want to give you one more thing to worry about!"

"So you're going behind my back and making decisions without me instead?"

Jen flushed. "You need to just calm down."

David looked around and noticed that some of Jen's coworkers were staring at them. Jen's voice dropped to a hiss.

"There isn't any money, David," she said. "What do you expect me to do?"

"You don't understand," David responded. "I have to have that membership. That's where my clients come from, and they can't see that I'm broke."

"How many ways do I have to tell you this? There's no money." Her voice was icy as she emphasized the final words. "I'm sorry. I really am, but it was one thing that we didn't have to pay right now. I didn't know what else to do."

She did not understand at all. David felt like his head would explode. He wanted to blame someone, and right now Jennifer was available.

He stormed out of her office without another word.

Thirty-Three

Water splashed off the tires as the Porsche surged through the small puddles in the dark roadway. There was a light sprinkling of water on the windshield. It must have rained while David was in the bar.

He had not wanted to go home. He could not face going to the shop. After having it out with Jen, David had gone where he always said he never would.

It had been years since David had been to a bar. He had never forgotten what it was like growing up in a house where alcohol dictated everything, so he had never been more than an occasional social drinker.

But he was tired of dodging bill collectors and doing everything he could to keep his shop afloat. The pressure of having to make payroll and the never-ending pursuit for the next customer was exhausting. David realized he had no idea what he was doing. He could fix a car, but running a business was another thing.

After a couple of hours nursing some pints and shots, David was coherent enough to realize that he'd had enough, especially since he was still driving his customer's car. He backed out of the parking stall and drove toward the road. The car bouncing off the edge of the curb jarred him. He wondered how he missed the exit as he pulled out into the roadway.

As David drove down the freeway, he started thinking about his financial problems again. When he was at the bar he had lost sight of his worries, but now the drinks must be been wearing off because that was all he could think about.

David hit the turn signal and pulled off the freeway toward his house. The off-ramp was a long, sweeping right-hand turn that corkscrewed tighter. David did not think he was speeding, but when the car settled into the turn, he realized he was coming in a little hot.

He downshifted to use the engine to slow the car. As soon as he released the clutch, the rear tires started to slip away from the asphalt at the same time he crossed a small puddle of water in the road. The rear tires continued to slip until the car began sliding across the thin layer of water.

David could feel the back end of the car lose traction, and then he made the mistake almost everyone makes—he took his foot off the gas. The moment the tires lost power, the car spun out of control. In a split second the car made a complete 360-degree spin and slammed into the guardrail.

Thirty-Four

It took David a minute after the collision to realize what happened. He was in the middle of the freeway off-ramp. Fortunately, no other cars were behind him. The car stalled, but he was able to get it started and move to the dirt on the side of the ramp.

David's heart was in his throat as he got out of the car to inspect the damage. It was not as bad as it could have been. The left front fender was curled in and the headlamp was hanging by the wires. He looked at the damage for a while trying to process what happened. He had not been driving recklessly, but with the first light rain of the year, there was just enough moisture to loosen the oil already in the road.

He thought he could drive the car home; it was only a couple of blocks to his house. Once he calmed down, he buckled his seat belt and put the car in gear. Before he pulled away, however, a bright red light lit him up from behind. He looked in his rearview mirror and saw the highway patrol.

I'm going to lose everything. David could only fixate on that thought as the officer walked up to the driver's seat. He shined his flashlight on David and then on the front fender as he inspected the damage. *What would Jen say? What about all the people who work for me? How can I ever look Zack in the face again?* The officer asked if David was hurt, then asked how much he had to drink. It was impossible to hide the odor.

The cop was polite, but he was a man of few words. He asked David to step out of the car to perform sobriety tests. Afterward, he simply said, "Here are your options, Mr. Parson."

David braced himself. Crashing a customer's car while drinking and driving was one thing; getting arrested could be the end.

"You're very close to the legal limit. You're not quite there, but you did crash. I could take you in, but if you can get someone to pick you up, I'm going to exercise some discretion tonight because no one got hurt."

The wash of relief almost made David stagger. "Thank you, sir." But whom should he call?

It was starting to rain again—hard. "I guess when it rains, it pours," David said to himself as his eyes fell on that bag of leftovers, still sitting on the passenger seat of the Porsche. He thought about it for a long moment, then got out his phone.

"Walter?"

"Yes?"

"I need your help."

Thirty-Five

When Walter arrived at the accident scene, he did not tease David as usual. Instead, he spoke to the police officer and made a phone call to a friend who owned a body shop. Walter knew a lot of people from making his morning rounds while trying to fill the void of retirement.

After the Porsche was towed to the body shop, Walter drove David home and explained that his friend would fix the minor damage without getting the insurance companies involved. But David knew he would still have to have an embarrassing conversation with the owner of the car, and here was another financial problem to add to the pile.

When Walter pulled up in front of David's house, David got out of the truck and stood inside in the truck's open door.

"Don't worry, we'll get the Porsche fixed," Walter said, expressing an empathetic side David had never seen.

"I don't know how to thank you, Walter." David felt defeated, even though he was grateful.

"Well," Walter cleared his throat. "I've been wanting to be more helpful—"

"This was more than helpful!"

"—but there's a condition."

David stared at him. "A condition?"

"And you're not going to want to do it, either. But it's happening. Tomorrow."

"Tomorrow?" David had no idea what he had gotten himself into.

"Yep, tomorrow." Walter said. "We're going fishing."

Thirty-Six

That is how David found himself, instead of going to the shop the next morning, walking up to Walter's house in the early morning hours. David had left early enough to avoid having to talk to Jen, who he was sure was still angry about the scene he had made at her office. She had not even said hello to him when he finally got home the night before. This day was a great way to avoid the whole thing.

When David got to the house, Walter was standing in the driveway trying to load a heavy cooler into the back of his boat.

"Give me a hand," Walter said. "I've got enough provisions for both of us."

"I think I'll pass on the beer today," David said with a grim face.

"Get in," Walter said as he pointed to the passenger side of his old Ford truck. They climbed in and headed to the lake.

It was a perfect day to spend on the water. It was already seventy-five degrees, with a gentle breeze creating small ripples across the lake. Because it was a weekday, they could claim Walter's favorite fishing spot all to themselves. Walter sat back in his seat with his pole resting against the side of the boat. He cracked open a can of cheap domestic beer.

David was beginning to relax as he took in the landscape and tried not to worry about his business. Birds were chirping as the sun started to peak over the hills surrounding the lake. The place was beautiful. It was obvious why Walter came here so often.

"So what's this all about?" David asked finally. "Why are you taking me fishing?"

"Remember what I was saying at the club yesterday?"

David winced. *Was it only yesterday?* "To tell you the truth, I wasn't listening to much of what you said. Something about bait?"

Walter laughed. "Well, you heard the most important part!"

Thirty-Seven

Walter did not miss a beat. "You need to build a list."

"I already did that!" David objected.

"All you have now is a current customer list. That's low-hanging fruit. If you want your business to grow, it's time to dig in and build a prospect list."

"A list of names?" David asked.

"Not just any list—you could use the phone book for that. You need a qualified prospect list."

"Qualified to do what?"

"Qualified to be your customer." Walter stirred through the bait in the pail and chose a hook for his line. "You don't want to just grab anybody. What you want are people who are interested in your services and who can pay for them—the kind of folks you can go back to again and again."

That sounds good. David nodded.

"There's a pen in my bag," Walter said. "Can you get it?" Walter stood up and peeled the marina slip off the inside of the boat's windshield.

David found the pen and handed it over, as Walter put the marina slip face down on his tackle box and then started to scribble. "There's a secret formula that runs just about every successful business," Walter said. "When you put that system in place, your business will grow."

"A secret formula?" David asked. "C'mon, Walter. Do you expect me to believe there are any secrets left?"

"I might sound like a late-night infomercial, but it must still be a secret. Otherwise there wouldn't be so many struggling businesses," Walter said, still writing as the boat rocked.

"Is it hard?"

"It's not complicated, but a lot of people are allergic to anything that doesn't come in an easy-to-swallow magic pill. It does take work. Look."

Walter had started a list on the back of the marina receipt.

1.

2.

3.

4. Follow-up

5. Offer

Walter put his pen down and handed the list to David. "So far, you've done these last two," he said. "What you've been doing with your former customers list and those postcards is following up. You already had a relationship with them, so now you can contact them whenever you want. You followed up with an offer. You can send offers to loyal customers whenever you want to drum up business. Does that make sense?"

David nodded, thinking hard.

"The beginning steps that you haven't done yet will allow you to create a constant stream of new customers that you can then follow up with forever. How does that sound?"

David's eyebrows rose. He said, "That sounds great!"

Thirty-Eight

Walter sat on his raised pedestal seat and put fresh bait on his line. After casting his line back in the water, he took the list back from David.

"The first three components on the list make up the lead-generation system. You need all three to make this work, but let's break it down one at a time." Walter wrote the word "bait" on the first blank line.

1. Bait
2.
3.
4. Follow-up
5. Sale

"Bait?" David asked. "At the club, I thought you were talking about fishing."

"Fishing and marketing have a lot in common," Walter said. "You use bait to attract and qualify the right people to add to your prospect list."

David stared blankly back at Walter.

"All right, I'll take it slow," Walter said. "Today we are using salmon eggs because we are fishing for trout, but if we were after largemouth bass, we would use minnows. Get it? Both fish are here in this same lake, but since we only want the trout, we choose the bait that works best with them."

"What should I use in my business?" David asked.

"Anything that your ideal prospect will pay attention to." Walter took a sip from his drink. "It may take some trial and error, but when you find the right bait, your business will thrive."

"Like a cheap oil change?"

"That worked great for your current customers. It might for new ones as well. Everyone needs their oil changed. Giving it away at a discount, or even a loss, to get them in the door is another way to build your list. What else could you do? What would make you stand out?"

David tried to look like he was thinking, but he had nothing.

Walter prodded him some more. "What are you really good at?" he asked. "What makes you different from other mechanics in town?"

"My location?"

Walter snorted. "No. Something about you, as a person, as a business owner, as a service provider. Why should I come to you instead of the lube or the tire places?"

It was David's turn to snort. "I'm not going to rip you off."

"That's perfect!" Walter said. "What about a free report, something like, 'The Seven Ways Your Auto Mechanic Is Ripping You Off'?"

That was something David ranted about frequently to anyone who would listen. But putting it all down on paper? David was intrigued by the idea, even though it seemed bold.

"So bait can be something free or low-priced?" David asked.

"Exactly," Walter said. "Free will attract more people, but the people who pay for something are usually better prospects. When you build your list by selling a low-cost item, you will miss out on some that are not ready today. It's a trade-off."

"What do I do with this bait?" David asked.

Walter grabbed the marina slip. He scribbled in the second line and tossed David the paper so he could read it.

Thirty-Nine

1. Bait
2. Lead generation
3.
4. Follow-up
5. Sale

David set the list down and slid it under the tackle box to keep it from blowing away in the breeze. "Okay..." he said. *Lead generation? That sounds like technical marketing talk.* He knew he was not going to be able to figure out what that was on his own.

Walter could see David was struggling. "Lead generation is kind of like dropping your line in a fishing hole that you know has a lot of the type of fish you want," he said. "In other words, you need to put your bait somewhere that your ideal prospect is."

"Like when I spend time at the country club?" David asked.

"Close. At the club, you're networking. That's like the fishing we're doing today—using one hook at a time, waiting for one fish at a time to bite. And that can be great. You meet one-on-one with new people until you find one that bites. It works, but it's terribly inefficient." Walter adjusted his line in the water. "If you're in a hurry, it's no good. Instead of fishing for one at a time, you need to throw out a large net and go after many fish."

"How do I do that?" David asked.

"One way is by running lead-generation ads—"

"But you told me not to run ads," David said.

"I said don't run branding campaigns. Lead-generation ads are different."

David's head began to swim. "What's the difference?" he asked.

"The difference is that lead generation works," Walter said smugly. "It's what will separate you from everyone who's pissing their money away on brand advertising."

"Gee, thanks," David laughed.

"Everybody has made that mistake," Walter said, "including me. They either stop marketing or continue throwing money at advertising that does not work. These brand campaigns on TV, magazines, and in your mailbox are essentially big business cards. They are never about the customer. They're about the company."

David frowned, not sure he was getting it.

"Look," Walter said. "You've seen the Goodyear Blimp buzzing around overhead, right?"

"Sure, the tire company. At ball games."

"They spend a lot of money broadcasting their brand name, but the blimp does not have an offer to inspire customers to visit a store and buy tires."

"So that's bad," David said.

"It's inefficient and wastes a lot of money. You need to generate leads," Walter said. "Instead of promoting your company, your ad sells the benefits of your bait. When you consider the ideas we had before—the free report and discounted oil change—both offer something to help your prospect. Your prospects don't care about your business. They only care about themselves."

"What you're saying," David clarified, "is that I have to advertise something that matters to them. Instead of advertising about my shop, I create an advertisement offering the bait. Is that the idea?"

Walter grinned. "That's it, David. You need a good headline to capture their attention, explain the benefits of your bait, and tell them how they can get it. It doesn't need to be complicated. Often it doesn't even need your company name or logo."

"Why would I skip the business name?" David asked. "What if someone needs my services? How will they call?"

"You can include that stuff, but it's usually a waste of expensive ad real estate."

David looked perplexed.

"Here's what I mean. When someone shoves a business card in your face, what do you normally do with it?"

"Honestly, I take it to be polite, but I throw it away when I get home," David said. He squirmed a little, remembering all those cards he'd handed out not that long ago.

"That's my point. Everyone else does the same thing. That's what happens with those ads. There is no reason for anyone to pay attention to them."

David got a little sick to his stomach when he thought about how much he'd spent on the contract with Sharon that went nowhere. "The bait changes that?" he asked.

"Exactly," Walter said. "With the right bait, your prospect has an incentive to pay attention to the ad. The bait makes them want to respond to the ad instead of dismissing it."

All of a sudden it made sense. It seemed so obvious that David wondered why he had never thought of it before. "This secret of yours—it's about making the customer want to contact you, rather than being talked into it. They call because—because—"

"Because there's something in it for them," Walter said.

Just then, Walter's fishing rod snapped toward the lake, bending in half and making a perfect U shape.

"You've got one!" David blurted out.

Walter dove for the pole and started reeling in his line as fast as he could. David grabbed the net sitting in the corner of the boat while Walter let the fish run some line out of his reel.

Walter went back and forth, reeling in and letting the line run out until they could see the trout fighting just under the surface. When the fish was within reaching distance, David bent over with the net in hand and nabbed it.

"Wow, Walter. That's the biggest fish I've seen come out of this lake," David said holding up Walter's prize catch.

Walter clapped him on the back. "It's all about the bait."

Forty

After catching that fish, David and Walter packed it up and headed home. They were both tired from being out in the sun. As they drove, David made a show of asking what the last thing on that list was, but Walter took one look at him practically falling asleep in the passenger seat and said he'd tell him later.

David was home by dinnertime. When he walked into the house, Zack was looking in the refrigerator for something to eat. Jennifer was sitting at kitchen table with a cup of coffee after her day of work.

Oh, yeah, David remembered. *I was a jerk.*

"How was the lake?" Jennifer asked coolly. "Molly told me you'd gone fishing."

Zack looked from one to the other as though he knew something was up.

"I caught dinner," David said, lifting his cooler with the fish, "and Walter taught me some more about marketing."

"That sounds interesting. Doesn't it, Mom?" Zack asked. "Tell us about it."

Jennifer didn't look impressed.

"What is this, a test?" David swatted at him, but he really did not want to talk about it because it still did not make total sense to him. He had to process it some more first.

"You know, I've been working on a website for you, Dad," Zack said.

"Really?" David did not know how a website would be useful. He had only reluctantly begun learning how to use the computer. Computers intimidated him. "You think people use the internet to find a mechanic?"

"People use the internet to find everything," Zack said. "Even old people."

"I'm not that old." David realized how often he called Walter the same thing. *I guess every generation thinks the prior one is out of touch.*

Jen put her cup down with a clunk. "If you boys clean those fish outside, I will cook dinner," she said.

David and Zack exchanged glances, and Zack took the fish to the backyard while David rummaged for the knives and cutting boards. Jen did not look at him.

David took a deep breath. "You know—"

"I know what?" she shot at him, her eyes flaring.

"—you have every right to be mad. I'm sorry. I was a jerk."

Jen pursed her lips. "Okay, fine. But I didn't do anything wrong."

"No, you didn't. I'm trying to work it all out. I was embarrassed and I took it out on you."

Her face softened—a little. "Let's just eat."

David took his fish-cleaning tools outside, giving her some space.

While they cleaned, Zack explained websites, social media, and email. David had only a vague idea how the internet was used in business. All the new terminology was quickly lost him.

"Dad, I had an entire semester about online marketing," Zack said. "Everyone uses social media and the internet to promote their business."

"How much does it cost?"

"Most of it is free."

David did not understand how all that could be free after he had been quoted thousands of dollars for a television commercial. But email was another interesting idea. David had just spent a ton of time and money mailing out postcards, and here was Zack explaining that David could be using email to do the same thing, but at no cost.

It was overwhelming. Was the internet the silver bullet David had been looking for?

Forty-One

The shop was quiet the next morning. David arrived earlier than usual and pulled on the long chains to roll the giant shop doors up. Molly was there, cheerfully making the first pot of coffee.

"Good morning!" she said. "Good day fishing?"

"I think so," David said. He dug the marina slip out of his pocket to show to her. "Walter was explaining this marketing stuff to me."

Curious, Molly listened to David's halting explanations of the concepts behind bait, lead generation, and then follow-up and offers. Speaking the ideas to someone else actually made it all clearer to David, although he was not that great at articulating it. He tried to recall everything Walter had said. He included some of the things Walter had said about measuring results, leaving out the colorful language Walter used to describe brand advertising.

"Honestly, I don't completely understand it," David said. "Walter believes I need a way to measure the amount of leads, customers, or sales that come in from each advertisement or promotion."

"I know about this stuff," Molly said. "The old mail-order guys used to do this. Now the internet marketers do the same thing."

"Walter said the same thing about mail order," David explained. "That's where he learned it. I doubt he knows anything about marketing on the internet. He doesn't even have a cell phone. But Zack knows all about it."

"What is this one?" she asked, pointing to the still blank #3 on the marina slip.

"I don't know. We didn't get to that one yet."

Molly crossed her arms. "I understand what you're saying, but you're not exactly selling gadgets from the back of a magazine," she said, as the door jingled. "Your business is different."

Walter was just walking in. "It's not different."

"Never thought I'd say this," David said as he grinned, "but I'm glad you're here. Would you explain this please?"

"Everyone thinks their business is different, but they're all the same," Walter said. "A business sells something that someone wants. It's that simple. The fundamentals of direct response marketing work for a doctor, or a mechanic—or someone selling gadgets from the back of a magazine."

Molly side-eyed him, but she was listening.

"So what's this #3?" David asked, pointing at the marina slip.

"The next item is critical." Walter cleared his throat to begin his lecture. "Few business owners understand how important this is, but it makes all the difference. In fact, if you don't do it, you're wasting your time and money when advertising or networking to generate leads for your business. I explained that you use lead generation to promote the bait you're using to attract prospects. But the part I didn't explain—"

"Why don't I just put the offer in the ad to begin with?" Molly interrupted. "Why complicate this with extra steps?"

"Hold your horses. You could include your offer, but the point of a lead-generation ad is to build a prospect list," Walter said. "Remember, the majority of people are in research mode. Did you tell her about that, David?"

"Kind of."

"No," said Molly.

So Walter took a moment to reiterate that eighty percent of people are researching before they buy. "If you only target buyers, you miss the remaining eighty percent of window shoppers."

Oh, right. David nodded. Now he remembered that "research mode" stuff.

Walter continued. "When you run a brand-advertising campaign, you get one chance that your prospect will act on your advertisement. If a prospect sees your ad and does not buy, then you've lost them unless they happen to see another of your ads some time. By using your advertising to build a list of prospects, you can get their contact information even while they're researching. Then you can follow up over and over until they move from the research phase to the buying phase."

"Do I follow up and send offers to my prospect list the same way I did with my customer list?" David asked.

"Yes, it's the exact same idea," Walter answered. "The only difference is that with prospects you need to spend more effort in your follow-up messages helping your prospects get to know you. Your prospects don't know you as well as your customers do, but otherwise, the follow-up and offer principles are the same."

"How do you get them to provide their contact information?" Molly asked.

"Your advertising will be exposed to a lot of different people," Walter said. "Unfortunately, most of them are not going to be interested in your services. To narrow down the list, your ad offers an immediate benefit to the prospect."

"That's the bait," David said. "I think I've got that part figured out."

"Bait allows you to generate leads. But then you've got to keep them. So, #3 is lead capture." Walter wrote those words on the marina slip.

1. Bait
2. Lead generation
3. Lead capture
4. Follow-up
5. Sale

"Voila!" Walter said, smiling proudly at the grubby marina slip. "Isn't it a thing of beauty?"

David and Molly stared down at the slip. "If you say so," Molly said.

"These five steps are like money in the bank," Walter said.

David scratched his neck. "So what is lead capture exactly?"

"Lead capture is the process you have in place to capture your prospect's contact information when they request the bait."

David raised his eyebrows, beginning to get impatient. "Can you just tell me what to do?"

"I can give you some simple ideas that will get you going today..." Walter said.

David perked up.

"But that will not help you in the long run," Walter said. "If you understand the philosophy, then you can experiment with it in your shop, or any business you own in the future."

"Is that the 'teach a man to fish' thing?" David asked.

"Exactly," Walter laughed. "You've got to do your own fishing. Let me give you a simple example to explain this process."

"Please," David said as he raised his palms upward as if he were expecting Walter to hand him something.

"Imagine a chocolate store in a mall," Walter said. "Outside the store is a sign that says 'Come in for a free box of chocolate.'"

Molly interrupted. "Free chocolate is the bait."

"Yes, and in this case the sign is generating leads from the foot traffic in the mall."

"Ah, so lead generation doesn't have to be from a paid advertisement?" David asked.

"Correct," Walter answered. "That's why I want you to understand the process. Once you get it, you can interchange the pieces with any advertising medium."

David nodded. He was beginning to see it.

Walter continued. "If someone walking through the mall sees the sign and wants chocolate, they will come in and get a free sample. Most companies hand out the sample without getting contact information. The prospect may buy something, but if they don't, there's no way to follow up to make them an offer later. If on the other hand, you get their contact information, you can follow up with them forever."

David looked uncertain. "Do I just ask?"

"You make it part of the process," Walter said. "If they want the bait, they have to leave their contact information. You can ask them to leave a business card or fill out a form, or use any method that works. In my day we used return postcards to capture leads. Later we started using twenty-four-hour phone recordings. Nowadays, businesses are using the internet."

"You know about the internet?" David said with a mischievous grin. "They didn't have the internet during World War II."

"More with the old man jokes?" Walter laughed. "The principles of marketing on the internet are no different than a sign in front of a chocolate store. The principles have been working for generations and are always the same regardless of the technology. The internet is just another medium to put your message in front of your prospects."

Forty-Two

David sat at his kitchen table with a laptop and typed a rough draft of a report with the title Walter suggested: "The Seven Ways Your Auto Mechanic Is Ripping You Off." David was a terrible writer, but he thought that if he could get something started, Molly could help clean it up.

When David sat down he had no idea what to write, but after working at it for a while he was surprised at how many ideas came pouring out. David had been in the automotive industry for nearly two decades and had seen a lot of unscrupulous behavior, so it was cathartic to vent on paper about the common mechanic scams. David really did want to protect his customers. *I suppose Walter would say that's part of my brand,* he thought.

After David finished the first draft, he started feeling overwhelmed again. With so many lead-generation and lead capture options, he did not know where to begin. He sat at the kitchen table staring out the window for about twenty minutes before he heard the repetitive thumping coming from outside. It took him a while to recognize the noise—it seemed like years since he last heard it.

David stepped outside and found Zack shooting baskets in the hoop attached to the side of the house. They had been playing together since Zack was old enough to dribble, but those days came to an end when Zack got busy in high school. David loved shooting baskets with his son, even though Zack was beginning to win more times than David wanted to admit.

Before long they were playing and it was tied 20 to 20. "Game point," David said as he started dribbling. David dribbled toward the basket and took an outside jump shot.

"Are you sure about that?" Zack asked as he rebounded the ball.

Zack faked a shot from the free-throw line that sent David jumping in the air. Zack dribbled around his dad and shot an easy layup to win the game.

"I let you win, Zack."

"It's been years since you've let me win, Dad," Zack said, smiling as he emphasized the word let. "Face it, Dad, I'm younger and faster."

David had to admit his son was growing up. He was proud of him.

"What have you been working on, Dad?" Zack asked.

"Let's go inside and get something to drink," David said. It was hard for David to admit he was no longer the all-knowing wise man that a father is to a young boy, but David was ready to put his pride aside. He put his arm around his son's shoulders as they walked toward the back-door of the house.

"Maybe you can help me," David said.

Forty-Three

David grabbed two sodas from the refrigerator, and they sat at the dining room table. David explained what he was trying to accomplish with his marketing funnel and each of the five components of a direct response marketing system.

Zack whipped out his laptop computer while David was talking. David looked at the slimline computer, which looked aerodynamic next to David's old, squarish laptop. Zack typed and clicked away at the mouse while his dad talked.

"Are you even listening?" David asked.

Zack turned the laptop around and pushed it across the kitchen table to his father. David looked and saw a basic website for Parson's Auto repair.

"How did you do that?" David asked.

"Been working on it. It's not complicated," Zack said. "I need your credit card."

David looked at the website, amazed what his son had created with his know-how. "How do you know how to do that?" David asked. David was still afraid he would push the wrong button and break something.

Zack used David's credit card and paid the small fee to host the website and set up an email autoresponder. Zack explained how the autoresponder web form could handle the lead capture and follow-up parts of Walter's system—a system Zack already seemed to grasp in its entirety. Zack pulled the computer closer and typed David's name and email into the form on the new Parson's Auto Repair website while David watched.

A moment later, David's phone chimed. He opened it up and saw an email that said "Test" in the subject line. David stared at his phone for a moment putting the pieces together.

"When someone puts their name in my website, they automatically get this email?" David asked, shocked by how easy this was.

"Exactly," Zack said.

"You did all of that while I was talking?" David asked his son.

"It's only a rough draft. You need to personalize it a bit more, but it's pretty much done," Zack said. "You can attach the report you wrote to this email."

"I can send emails to anyone who requests the report?" David asked. He was beginning to see the possibilities and envisioned how much easier—and cheaper—it would be to email offers to his customers than to send them in the mail.

Zack clicked away from the website and brought up a social media site. After scrolling through pictures of babies, angry political rants, and funny videos of dogs, David was confused.

How to be Rich — Chuck Rylant

Jennifer walked into the kitchen while the boys were staring at the computer. "Social media, huh?" she stated "I'll bet you love that." David smiled at her ruefully. When she saw David's sour look, she added, "Don't be such a scrooge."

He was glad she was being a little playful. He reached for her hand, and she came over to stand beside him and to straighten the hair on the top of his head. He squeezed her and she squeezed back. Relieved, he tried to make conversation. "I know this social media thing is supposed to be great," he said, "but I don't see how it can possibly help my business. What do I do with it?"

"You get your friends to click 'like' on your page," Zack said.

"And then what?"

"You post comments and photos and stuff," Jennifer answered.

"What's the point of that?" David asked.

Jennifer and Zack grinned at each other, and all three of them laughed.

"I'll manage the page, Dad," Zack said. "The important thing is that you have one."

Forty-Four

So now David had another ad buy to think about. But this one would be very different.

Instead of disbursed brand advertising in multiple wide-area newspapers and magazines, he would focus on hyper-local opportunities. Molly and Zack did some research on what would be the best publications in which to place a few small classified ads.

Zack figured out how to list the offer for the report for free on neighborhood websites and on a classified ad site David had never even heard of where you could list for free whatever you were selling. It was both local and international, which did not make sense to David, but Molly understood completely.

There was also a great community paper David leafed through all the time that had not even been in Sharon's ad buy. He'd forgotten all about it, even though it came to his mailbox every week. It went to people right in town for free, once a week. The cost of a classified ad that would run for five weeks was about a tenth of just one of

Sharon's daily newspaper ads. Still, David knew he had to discuss it with Jen.

Molly had done some great work on the report, turning David's disorganized writing into something that looked attractive and professionally crafted. She was becoming increasingly indispensable, but when he got home to talk with Jen about money, things did not look good for his being able to keep Molly.

"I don't know, David," Jen said, leafing through a stack of bills. They were both too tired to cook dinner, so David sat down next to his wife and ate leftovers. "We've got payroll, the bill for the lifts—which we must pay in two weeks—shop rent, and utilities, and we've got to set some aside for Zack's tuition or he'll never get to go back. I don't see how we can do another round of ads."

David blew out a breath to decompress. He felt like he was so close to making all Walter's suggestions really pay off.

Jen reached over and rubbed his arm. "I think we might have to face it—it might be time to let Molly go."

David buried his face in his hands. "I can't do that. She's so important to all the work we're doing right now."

"Couldn't Zack do most of what she's doing anyway?"

David looked at her bleakly. "Is there nothing left? Nothing in retirement or anywhere?"

Jen joked, "There's the cookie jar."

Years before, David and Jen had started throwing all their extra change into a big glass cookie jar in the pantry, just to keep it from clogging up their wallets. When Jen mentioned it now, David jumped up to get it.

It was about two-thirds full. He and Jen looked at each other, and then David unscrewed the top and poured it all out onto the table.

Many piles of quarters, dimes, nickels, and pennies later, they discovered it was about ten dollars more than David would need to place that tiny classified in the local newspaper offering the free report.

"How about it?" he asked Jen.

She smiled wearily. "Go for it."

Forty-Five

David walked into the shop the next morning with more on his mind than he could keep up with. He felt like a juggler with balls in the air that might slip through his hands at any moment.

He got Zack going on writing up the classified ad and placing the order. The little ad would go in right away, not only in the print edition, but also on the paper's website. Zack got that up and going in no time, but David did not know what to expect for results.

In the meantime, he needed some big jobs fast to cover all that was looming at the end of the month, especially the payment due for the lifts. But he had nothing. He sat at the office desk staring straight ahead with a blank look on his face.

"Why the 1,000-yard stare, David?" Molly asked when she brought him some receipts to sign.

David snapped out of his trance. He did not have the heart to mention that he had been considering letting her go. "I need to come up with another offer for our customers, but I'm drawing a blank."

"How about a $1,000 discount on brake repair?" Molly said while she looked up prices for parts.

"Something wrong with your brakes?" David asked.

"They've been making a scraping sound," Molly said. "There was nothing on the schedule so I finally got Tony to take a look. Turns out they are really bad, so I have to replace all the rotors. It's going to cost a fortune."

"We'll get it fixed at cost, you know that," David said automatically. "But you know better. Why didn't you have them checked out before they got so bad?"

"It's not like there's a warning light for your brakes," Molly explained. "Between work and shuttling family all over town, brakes are the last thing on my mind. Even with the shop discount, it's going to cost me a fortune to fix them."

"You needed a reminder—" David stopped himself suddenly. Many pieces of the marketing puzzle seemed to fall from the sky, right into his lap.

Forty-Six

"**M**olly, I need you to do something for me." David said. He got excited the more he thought about it. The idea was crystallizing in his mind with each second that passed.

She looked up from her computer. "Now?"

"Yes, now." He could not wait to get it started. "I want you to write a letter."

"A letter about what?"

"It is from you to our customers," David said. "I want you to write the story you just told me about your brakes. Include everything about being busy with family and neglecting your car. Tell them how much money you would have saved if you had checked it sooner."

"That's kind of embarrassing," Molly said. "Like you said, I should have known better."

"Put that in the letter too," David said. "That's exactly why you're writing the letter, because you realize how easy it is to overlook important things. If you work at an auto shop and can forget to inspect your brakes, imagine how easy it is for everyone else to forget."

"I don't know how to write a letter like that," Molly resisted.

"Neither do I," David said. "In your letter, just pretend you're talking with your best friend over coffee and express your worry that she could make the same mistake. And at the end," David slapped the counter for emphasis, "let them know we are providing a free brake inspection to all our past customers."

Light dawned on Molly's face. She started writing.

Forty-Seven

After the weekend, David got to the shop early to get a head start on his marketing before customers arrived. He could feel the early-morning cold when he grabbed the steel chains to raise the shop door.

"Did you get off your ass and work on your marketing?" Walter asked with a grin as he walked in.

"Good morning to you too, old man." But David was proud of what they had been doing. Soon, he'd filled Walter in on the new website, the classified ad, the "Seven Ways" report, the automated online response feature, and Molly's letter.

"Impressive!" was all Walter said.

"Do you think it will work?" David asked, seeking approval like a boy would from his father.

Walter shrugged. "How should I know?"

"Oh, come on!" David said. "Throw me a bone here!"

"There's only one way to find out if it's working," Walter said. "Test and measure. Does that website track how many people visit it and put their name in those boxes?"

"Um..." David said. He had no idea.

"It does," Zack answered from the cramped office. "And we can tell from the response if it's from the classified ad or from the website itself, or from some other place. We're set up to track phone calls, too, and to always ask where they heard about us."

David and Walter walked over to join him.

"Excellent," Walter said. "That's how it's done. Smart boy you got there!"

"That makes one of us," David said, grinning.

Zack continued, "We're going to measure at every stage to see what kinds of ads make people click all the way through, which ones have too many abandons—"

"Huh?" David asked.

"Abandons. Like if they get part way through a transaction and then quit. We have to track those."

Walter was nodding. "That's more sophistication than we ever had."

"If we run this ad and it sends people to this phone number and website, we can measure how many people went to the web page or called. If all of them use the internet and none use the phone, then we know we don't have to worry about staffing the phone as much."

"Aw, people still use the phone, don't they?" David asked.

"We don't know," Zack said. "We'll see. They told me in school it's important not to rely on our preconceived notions about what works, but to actually let the data tell us. We could be surprised."

Walter was nodding vigorously. "And you'll need to continue tracking your prospects throughout your funnel," he said. "Measure how many of the callers or web visitors leave their contact information. Then measure how many respond to your offers. Never stop measuring so you can continually refine your system until you have a well-oiled machine."

"So what about this?" David asked. He told them that he had been looking into ads in his church's weekly newsletter. It did not reach as many people as the newspaper ad, but it was also not as expensive.

"Expense is relative," Walter said. "Something that costs a lot of money but works well may end up being less expensive than a cheaper ad that does not work. You won't know until you try."

"I'm just trying to figure out which is best."

"That's the million-dollar question advertisers have been asking for years," Walter answered. "My answer is: There is no best. The real question to ask is: Which media does your ideal customer pay attention to?"

"How do I find that out?"

"Start with a little common sense," Walter said. "If you're after people my age, the internet probably won't be effective, but you may have luck with the local newspaper. Stay-at-home moms might read parenting magazines or the coupon mailers. They're probably also using the internet. There are too many options to cover them all, but I think you get the idea."

"But how do I pick?" David asked, frustrated. He wanted direct answers.

"After you narrow the list down with common sense, you have to test and see what works. Sometimes you get it right and sometimes it flops. That's the game. The important thing is that you track the results." Walter clapped him on the back. "This is just the beginning, David. Expect a lot of trial and error before you get it right. If an advertisement doesn't work, it still brings you one step closer to the right ad. It's hard to swallow spending money on ads that don't work, but it is often part of the process and why being able to measure results is so important."

Just then Zack's phone vibrated. He grabbed it to look at the notification. "We got another ping!" he said, excitedly. "Someone responding to the classified."

"Another one?" David asked, surprised.

"Yeah," Zack said, like he was giving a birthday present. "They've been going all weekend."

David gaped as his son high-fived him, right in front of Walter.

Forty-Eight

By the end of Monday, David was feeling optimistic. They had been all set to prepare the Molly letter for the mail when Zack pointed out that their database already had a bunch of email addresses for many of their clients, plus all the new contacts from the classified ad. It would save money to send Molly's letter to those clients through the internet. In the end, David decided to "snail mail" (as Zack called it) to everyone on his list, even those where they had email addresses. He wanted to contact them multiple ways.

David was rightfully proud of Molly's letter, but the real reason he was so gung-ho about it was because he had no other choice. It had to work.

On Tuesday, David was closing up with Molly after Zack and the mechanics had gone home when an unwelcome visitor stormed in.

"What is this garbage?" yelled Frank, as he pushed the shop door open with a loud jangle of the bells.

"What are you doing here?" David asked, heated. This was totally out of left field.

"I saw your classified!" Frank threw the local newspaper on the counter.

Molly ducked her head and tried to look like she was working on the computer.

"It's just an ad," David said.

Frank's face was red with anger. "Yeah, with some smarty-pants report about other mechanics ripping you off. What's that supposed to mean? When you learned everything you know from me!"

"I wasn't talking about you," David responded. "That's your problem if you think I was."

"Who else are people going to think you're talking about?"

"I haven't worked with you for years!"

Frank puffed out his chest. "You worked *for* me. And by the looks of things, you never should have left."

"All right." The loudness of David's voice surprised even himself. "That's enough. This conversation is over."

Frank blustered a bit and then sharply turned around and left, with another parting jangle.

Once he was gone, Molly waved her hand in front of her face. "Phew! A bit early in the day, right?"

The smell of stale beer still lingered even after Frank had gone.

David shrugged, not wanting to admit his own recent brush with alcoholic folly. "That's his problem."

Forty-Nine

But by Thursday evening, David started to think maybe Frank was right. Not a single customer had called to schedule a free brake inspection. There was one more day until the deadline, but David expected that he would have gotten a response by now. When he got home, he was losing hope. He felt defeated.

If the letter did not bring in enough business, David would have to close the shop doors for good. As painful as it would be, David was already wondering if a job back at the dealership was indeed his only option.

David did not say much to Jennifer before taking a shower and crawling into bed. He was exhausted, but not sleepy because the stress was getting to him. He pretended to be asleep when Jen came to bed, and soon he heard her peaceful breathing beside him. But he could not sleep himself.

He tossed and turned on the bed for what seemed like hours. Finally he got up and aimlessly started wandering around the house.

He just could not think straight. As he went through room after room, it finally started to hit him how much they could potentially lose. Jen never talked about the mortgage or their living expenses or taxes, but those were part of the mix, too. She was doing as much as she could to cover it all with her salary.

The worries swirled around in David's head. Molly. Zack. His marriage. The shop. It began to feel overwhelming.

He found himself in the kitchen, at the fridge. Opening the door, the light from inside made him squint and the cold hit his face like a reality check.

There was a six-pack or two of beer in there from some of Zack's friends. David almost reached for a can. Instead, he let the fridge door close.

He stared at the big calendar on the door that Jen had up there to keep track of their schedules. It had a big photo of someone's idea of a cute cat. Jen loved cats.

At least I don't have a cat depending on me, he thought suddenly. The idea was actually a relief.

He turned to look around the kitchen.

At least we've got plenty of food.

He kept turning in place, looking all around him. He was surrounded by their house, their cars, their neighborhood.

And a lot of good things have happened, he thought. *What about that account agent who agreed to give us the month extension? What about that cop?*

David took a deep breath. He still had the car lifts at the shop. He had not gotten arrested. What a fiasco that would have been. He kept thinking of good things.

And what about Walter, willing to give me some pointers? And Molly, willing to work for way less than she could get somewhere else? And Zack, willing to come home and help out? And Jen?

He got choked up thinking about Jen. In fact, as he thought over the past months, there were millions of little things that had helped him. Why would all that happen if he were only going to fail now?

The answer was: He was not going to fail. The answer was: He would figure it out.

As David turned back to stare at that calendar on the freezer, with its corny cat photo that Jen loved so much, he zeroed in on the next day, Friday. He saw suddenly that it was one of a whole bunch of Fridays. In fact, the entire column of that day of the week just shone out at him, like it was highlighted or bolded.

Then, David smacked himself on the forehead.

Fifty

Alittle bit later, when Jen and Zack got up, they found David scribbling on a copy of Molly's letter that he had printed out from their computer.

"Look at this," he said, before they even said good morning. "I screwed up again!" But he did not sound upset. He sounded energized. "What were the three things Walter told me?"

Zack rumpled his own hair sleepily. "I thought you said it was five things?"

"No, before that." David lifted up his hand and put out his fingers as he counted. "When you do an offer, you need: one, a reason; two, a call to action; and three—" here he jabbed the three fingers into the air, "scarcity!"

Jen and Zack looked at each other.

"Look! Look!" David pushed the letter across the counter at them. "No scarcity!"

Jen said, "But you have a deadline."

David read it out loud. "'To get your free brake inspection, come in or call before Friday.'"

"Yeah, today," Zack said, frowning.

"No! That's the problem. I did not make it clear that it was *this* Friday. People could think it's any Friday—in fact, they could think the deal goes on forever."

Jen and Zack stood there, bracing themselves for David's angry or discouraged reaction. But instead, David slapped his hand on the counter.

"And," he said, "I know exactly what to do about it!"

Fifty-One

David walked into the office with Zack right behind him and went straight to his desk. He picked up the phone from the desk and pinched it between his ear and shoulder. Molly said good morning to them, and David nodded his head to say hello. Rummaging through the mess on his desk, he found the printed out customer list and started dialing the first name.

"Good morning, Ms. Wilcox," David said into the phone. "This is David from Parson's Auto Repair."

After a brief pause, David said, "I'm following up on a letter Molly sent you. Today is the last day to schedule the free brake inspection before it goes back up to the normal price of forty-nine dollars."

Molly and Zack watched David, trying to figure out what he was doing.

"Oh, you did?" David said into the phone. "That's great. I have the schedule here in front of me. How does Tuesday at 3:00 work for you? ... Yes, I'll tell Molly." David hung up and turned to Molly, with a smile from ear to ear.

"What did she say?" Molly asked.

"Ms. Wilcox told me to thank you for the letter. She thought it was sweet. She has never received anything like it before. She wanted to call after she read it, but she forgot." David clapped in triumph. "And...she booked an appointment!"

"What happened, Dad?" Zack asked. "Why did you think to call her?"

"Last night I read the letter," David said. "It was a great letter, so I was surprised that we didn't get any responses. But then I realized the deadline was weak, and we didn't put the normal price of the brake inspection in the letter. People might think that it's always free."

"So you're going to call everyone?" Molly asked.

"Walter told me to continually follow up with offers," David said. "We can send more letters, but I'm in a hurry, so why not just pick up the phone? Isn't that a way to follow up?"

"Well, give me some of that list," Molly said.

"Me, too," Zack chimed in.

They called the entire customer list. By the end of the day they had completely filled all the mechanics' schedules for the upcoming week. When each mechanic's calendar was booked, they worked on booking David's, too.

By evening, David was exhausted. It took a lot of energy calling customers all day. It was not exactly telemarketing cold prospects, but it was only a few steps removed. It was not fun, nor was it something David wanted to make a habit of. Now he knew why Walter suggested letters, but he also saw the process in action.

Fifty-Two

Every day of the following week, all three of the mechanic's bays had cars in them. The shop was buzzing with the sound of pneumatic air wrenches hammering away as David and the other mechanics removed the lug nuts on cars suspended in the air.

Walter walked in while David was pulling tires off the car he was working on. "I had to park in the street because your lot is full of cars. What the hell did you do, David?"

"I have to admit I was wrong about you, Walter," David jabbed while smiling at Walter. "That marketing stuff you taught me actually works."

David was in a playful mood. He had not felt this good in a long time. The emotional rollercoaster of being a business owner was wearing him out, but today he was charged.

"Where did all of these cars come from?" Walter asked.

"I sent out that letter for free brake inspections," David said. "That got them in here, but many of them needed brake repairs and other work too. It's amazing."

Walter folded his arms across his chest as a big smile stretched across his face. He was proud of his student and enjoyed watching David's success, while feeling partly responsible for it. "Most business owners never reach out to their customers," Walter said. "People are busy. They want to be reminded that you are there for them."

"Honestly, I was a little uncomfortable that people would be put off by my new marketing, but they've been thanking us," David said. "That last letter really struck a chord, and they seem grateful for the offer."

"It was a great letter," Walter said. "I read the one you sent to my house."

"Thanks, Walter," David said soaking up the compliment. "We're also getting steady responses to that classified ad, and capturing all the information we need to keep following up."

"Terrific!" Walter asked. "There's only so much business growth you can achieve from just a current customer list. You'll always need those new prospects."

"One question," David said.

"Only one?"

David grinned. "How often should we follow up? I know it could get irritating to hear from us too much."

"Not only that, but if you're contacting them all the time, you could dilute that feeling of scarcity." Walter leaned against the tool bench. "Walk me through what you've got so far," he said. "What are the follow-up steps?"

"Right now, it's just three emails. The first is a greeting that introduces them to the free report. Then there are two more emails. One is about oil changes and the other discusses the other engine fluids. They explain how often to change the fluids and the costs of ignoring them."

"Add several more follow-up steps, but make them about different things," Walter suggested. "Send the free report by email, but you might also send it by regular mail."

"Why mail and email?"

"The more times you contact your prospects the better," Walter explained. "And the more different forms of media you use, the better your chance of reaching all of your prospects. Also, don't forget those personal touches, like for their birthday or even for their anniversary of becoming your customer."

David nodded his head.

"Send the oil change email out and follow it up with the oil change letter you've already written," Walter explained.

"The one I sent my customers?"

"Yes, just tweak it for noncustomers. You've got to learn to recycle all of the work you're doing to save time," Walter said.

"That makes sense. I'll get Zack and Molly to organize all that. They're wizards at keeping me organized."

"Good. You keep following up with customers for as long as it remains profitable," Walter said. "That's what your job is. It's not to be out here getting dirty for the rest of your life. Work on cars for as long as you enjoy it, but where you'll really find freedom as a business owner is when you move from being the technician to the marketer of your business."

Fifty-Three

When David returned to the country club, he felt a sense of calm he had not experienced in a long time. With all of his bills paid up, he was able to walk onto the grass and enjoy being under the warm sun without any stress. He forgot how much he enjoyed taking a break from the shop and being outside.

Walter had a small cooler strapped to their golf cart. He reached in and pulled out a can of soda and tossed it to David. David cracked it open and took a sip.

"I need to thank you, Walter," David said. "What you taught me has changed my life."

"In what way?"

"I look at my business completely differently now." David said. "I used to think the important part was working on cars, but now my focus is working *on* my business instead of *in* my business. That is a game changer."

"Not everyone is willing to invest that time, but it pays off," Walter said.

"I have more free time now," David said. "Remember that Camaro on blocks in my garage?"

"The '67, right?" Walter asked.

"I bought it four years ago to work on with Zack, but I got so busy with the shop," David said. "There was never time. When I was a kid, my dad and I used to work on his project car. I enjoyed it and I wanted Zack to have the same experience."

"You've worked hard to build your marketing system," Walter said. "Enjoy the fruits of your labor, but be careful. It's easy to slack off. Instead, you have to keep improving the system. What works today won't always work. Things change. People change and so does technology. Don't get complacent. You've only scratched the surface." Walter took a sip from his drink. "You've got the fundamentals. There is still a lot more to learn."

Fifty-Four

David and Zack worked a couple of hours each day writing ads and testing headlines and media sources. They rented mailing lists and used postcards to generate leads. They built several websites and wrote various free reports, and Zack made a short film using the same format as the free report. They put the video online and used it interchangeably with the printed report.

A lot of the things they tested were complete flops, but a few worked well. They kept the winners and ditched the losers. David was no longer surprised when things did not work. Now David knew that failed experiments are part of the process. They kept moving forward.

David was happy with his business success, but the most important part was that he spent a lot of time with his son. They worked on the business, but also spent hours together in the garage finally working on that Camaro. They wanted to get it finished before Zack headed back to school for the next semester.

As they tinkered away one evening after closing, a completely unexpected visitor showed up.

David and Zack had just removed the hood to allow room to lower the new engine into the Camaro, hoisting it into the air with a cherry picker. While Zack was pushing the hoist forward, David guided the engine into the car. David watched closely in the engine compartment, making sure the heavy, swaying engine did not smash into anything.

David could hear a car engine shut off and a car door shut, but he was engrossed in the hanging engine.

Then Zack said in surprise, "Grandpa?"

"What?" David jolted up to see Frank standing there.

"How are you?" Frank asked, and he hugged Zack.

"I haven't seen you in a while, Grandpa!"

"I haven't been around much lately," Frank said. "I guess I've been working too much."

David stood there unsure what to say. An unexpected visit from his dad at home was unheard of.

"Can you grab Grandpa a beer from the mini-fridge?" David asked.

"No beer for me, Zack," Frank replied. "But I would like a cold soda if you've got one."

Zack went inside to get the drinks. David and Frank looked at each other awkwardly.

"No beer?" David asked.

"I stopped drinking a couple of months ago," Frank said. "Right after—well, right after the last time we talked."

The time you came over to pick a fight with me, you mean. David snorted a little, but he was listening.

Frank cleared his throat. "I should have quit a long time ago. You leaving the shop should have been my wake-up call, but I didn't pay attention. And I've been letting the business spiral downhill for years." But he looked around David's shop proudly. "Been noticing what you're doing in your business, though. It's good stuff."

Frank was never one to open up, nor was he generous with compliments. "Uh, thanks," David said. "And you did the best you could after Mom died."

Their eyes met, and then they both quickly looked away.

"Maybe," Frank said, his voice hoarse. "I'm thinking of closing down, though. It's time for me to slow down a bit."

"You've had that business as long as I can remember," David said. "Are you sure?"

"Yeah," Frank said. "Glad I've got a great shop over here to refer my customers to."

David hid that he was choking up as Zack returned with the drinks.

"Set those drinks on the bench, Zack," David said. "And let's get to work on this animal."

They worked together that afternoon, all three generations, to make the final connections and get the engine humming. It was a fine moment when David could say, "Get behind the wheel, Zack. It's ready."

Zack turned the key. After the engine cranked over a few times, the fuel finally reached the carburetor and the engine rumbled to life.

A Word from Chuck

There were many topics I wanted to include in this book, but I had to accept that no single book can cover everything. While editing, I had to remove several chapters and gloss over certain topics to keep the story moving forward and focused on my original intent.

The purpose of the book is to introduce the reader to the principles of direct response marketing through an entertaining story. I also want the reader to be able to relate to some of the emotional hardships that many small-business owners experience.

Business and marketing is complicated, with many nuances that vary from business to business; however, these principles can be transferred to virtually any field and applied to every form of advertising medium. Technology will always change, but the fundamentals will remain true.

For the person new to this style of marketing, I hope this book provides an understanding of the fundamentals and serves as a starting point for your continued education. For the experienced marketer, I hope you enjoy the story line and welcome the unique way I laid out the fundamentals of direct response marketing.

I encourage you to continue learning more by visiting **www.ChuckRylant.com** where you can find free articles, including a streamlined report outlining all of these marketing principles. Readers of this book can also apply for a free 45-minute one-on-one coaching session.

Bonus Material

As a reader of this book, you are entitled to FREE advanced training and coaching. The book that you hold in your hands is only the beginning. There are a ton of FREE articles containing powerful information that will take you and your business to the next level. Before you get distracted, visit www.ChuckRylant.com and claim your free bonuses.

www.ChuckRylant.com

About the Author

Providing marketing advice was not something I ever planned to do—it happened organically.

When I was building a financial planning practice, I studied marketing obsessively. I returned to college to earn a master's degree in business administration (MBA). I read most of the business books multiple times, invested in tons of online training programs, and participated in numerous $10,000-plus marketing seminars and coaching programs.

All of that training was invaluable, but the real lessons came through the trial and error of implementing the strategies I was learning. I have owned various businesses throughout my life. Some ventures have thrived, others have gotten by, and some have crashed and burned, but as painful as the failures were, they always provided the greatest lessons.

As my coaching practice grew, I acquired multiple small-business owner clients, and the conversation always evolved from managing their money to bringing in more. At the same time, I also started getting invitations to give marketing talks at financial planning conferences. The demand from my clients and other financial advisors inspired me to begin formally offering marketing coaching and also develop marketing training programs.

While working with clients, I could not find a single, low-cost resource that business owners could consult to learn the fundamentals of direct response marketing so that we could use our coaching time most efficiently. That led me to write this book, which I hope provides a starting point for entrepreneurs who want to begin their study of direct response marketing.

Acknowledgements

I want to give special thanks to Laura Matthews for helping me edit and craft this story. Without her patience, hard work, and brilliant understanding of the art of storytelling, I would have never completed this book. Thank you, Laura, for everything you have taught me through the years and helping me make this project happen.